I SHOULDA ATE THE ECLAIR

I Shoulda Ate the Eclair

by

Milt Gross

CHICAGO   ZIFF-DAVIS PUBLISHING COMPANY   NEW YORK

PRINTED IN THE UNITED STATES OF AMERICA

To Anne,
and the three little eclairs,
Herb, Jerrold, and Steve.

I SHOULDA ATE THE ECLAIR

1

STROLLING down the street, in conjunction one with the other, walked the Mister with the Missus Figgits. Strolling in the front was Mister Figgits. Trailing in the back was Missus Figgits.

1

Balmy was the day with pleasant. Noon-time it was almost. Populated gradually was the streets. By the sidewalks, loiterers.

On the corner, Cuthbert Wendelhorse . . . . frozen for duration to his job . . . . but for the last eighteen months, de-frosted.

Nods with bows with salutations, it made to the neighbors, Mister Figgits. To the Missus Tranifatts and Junior, Golden Gloves Tranifatts, Missus Figgits cheerfully called good morning.

Just bouncing out from their new post-war folding bed, the Bimbergs gave a wave politely to the Mister with the Missus Figgits.

Politely it raised Mister Figgits in return to Missus Bimberg, the hat. Politely from the roadway was raised to Missus Figgits, from Mister Ginder, the slot-machine tycoon, his hat. On account Mister Ginder was too tied up at the moment to raising it himself.

Amused sat Missus Bowser, in a book.

And up a ways, also in a book, was gradually her dog Bismark, even more amused.

Past the Mister with the Missus Figgits, walked their new neighbor, the mysterious one.

"Good morning, neighbor Beezwaks," gave greetings Mister Figgits .... "and how fare you this bright sunny morning?"

"Bah! .... Women!" gave snorts from aggravation Mister Beezwaks. "Back and forth, back and forth, all day long, day by day, week in, week out, I try by the beauty parlor to make appointments. Tramp, tramp, tramp. March, march, march. Boots, boots, boots! Did you get a appointment? Did Wallace get a appointment? Bah! The country's got two strikes on it."

"Only two strikes," gave interruptions Missus Figgits, "would make it seem already like everything is settled."

"That's what I keep telling the Missus," gave answers Mister Beezwaks, "but she's all wrapped up in her own problems .... Bah! I think I'll try the post office instead."

"He'll never squeeze it through the slot," mused Mister Figgits.

"Mind your own business," cautioned Phoebe, while up the block they both proceeded.

And seeing twice a year his dentist, they encountered on the corner, Mister Yifnif.

"Cheerio!" gave exclamations Mister Figgits.

Responded Mister Yifnif: "So soon'll coming Television, this'll gonna be a lot less complicated!"

"Could was!" it made agreements Mister Figgits. What it waved to him a greeting with the tail, Mister Fink, the iceman's horse:

"Good morning Mister and Missus Figgits!"

For a chat they stopped with friend, De Pester . . . . formerly
by a Aircraft Carrier a Landing Signal Officer . . . . now by the

Amusement Park directing landings.

Inside from the Park was busy one from the Double-Feature Attractions. Making on the telephone a date, a blind one.

So it kept on strolling Fenimore with Phoebe Figgits. Congratulations did they offer to the Mister with the Missus Gillie,

on the new house which the friendly couple had just picked up.

"Confidentially," gave chuckles Mister Gillie, "It's a steal."

While in front, sat little Tillie Gillie breaking in for Mamma, a new pipe.

"My my!" gave banters Mister Figgits. "It breaks in little Tillie now a pipe! And when you'll growing up to be so big like me, my little one, what will you gonna do then?"

To which it interloped a answer, Missus Figgits.

"Go on a diet!"

Marching it continued Mister Figgits. From the rear came petulantly queries from the Missus Figgits.

"Must you always walk in front; it should know everybody that we're married?"

In order not to disturbing the peace, it changed Mister Figgits the subject with remarks:

"Did you noticed, my little chickadilly, this morning in the paper. It stood a article, that soon will be on the market a automobile a brand new type. With only three wheels yet!"

To which came answers from the Fluffnik family:

"What's new about that?"

In this manner it became noon. So it decided Mister Figgits to inviting Phoebe, they should sojourn by Felix in the Cafe for a slight snatch lunch.

"Noon-time, little pussy-bunny," gave chuckles Fenimore to Phoebe by the chin. "Time for lunch you know!"

"I know," gave answers Missus Figgits. "I see by Felix from the kitchen, a exodus mice, all heading for the Beanery across the street!"

"Ha ha ha," gave chuckles Mister Figgits. . . . "A sense from humidor is for digestions greatly aidful. This I read in a paper. Oh yes my dear, many things you reading in the paper, educational. It stands also there a article, a scientific one! Did you know dear, that difference colors could affecting difference people differently? I mean it could affecting by them the peace with harmony. I mean my love, that sometimes is by two people the temperment incompactible. He has a hobby maybe to read in bed whodunits. By her is a diversion to turn loudly on at the same time, the radio. This is causing in between them distention. So, in this case, they adopting for themselves new color schemes. And then they living together, much better in rappaport with each other."

"My my my!" gave exclamations Phoebe. "So remind me! We must paint green to-night our faces, and purple the posteriors. Then, in the love seat we could be forever after more compactible. What else, professor?"

"Well here we are in front from the Cafe," changed lightly the subject Mister Figgits. "Give a look a screwball on a soapbox. Let's we should give a listen."

"Beware from the Atomic Bomb!" gave roars the speaker.

"Beware the bomb! It could destroy the world . . .! Beware, beware!"

"Pfooey!" gave comments Mister Figgits.

"Pfooey?" gave questioningly Phoebe.

"A racket!" made pronouncements Mister Figgits. "He's probable auditioning the bewares it should catch him maybe for a Barber Shop quartette, a talent scout."

"You'll hallucinate me maybe the reason for this eminince opinion."

"With pleasure lambie-pie! Pure with simple this! Let's to our own knitting stick! And leave them to theirs! For lunch I think I'll desiring chicken's croquettes, a slice pineapple with a hole in the middle, and for ten cents coffee, in a cup!"

For a moment it paused Mister Figgits to admire in the Cafe window, carved out on a watermelon, the entire Battle from Gettysburg.

"And now my dear, let's we should trespass into the Cafe, where elegantly we'll tie on the nose bag . . . . Hm, bombs . . . . warnings . . . . bewares . . . . Pfooey again. What for do they let crackpots to get all steamed up the public? All it desires the public, is, it should be left alone. It should do full with honest, a day's work. It should keep to the nose, the grindstone . . . . With useful, worthy, worthwhile occupations.

By now they had arrived inside. A look around gave Phoebe with a comment:

"This must be, I assume, examples from the worthy worthwhile occupations."

Daintily she gave a wave her arm in order she should indicate to Fenimore about the place the doings from the occupants from the cafe.

By the Pin-ball machine near the bar, it gave wobbles—a gentleman, slightly drunk! Sightings on the Special-When-Lit he was making, through a vanity mirror belonging to his girl friend. Like he should be a Deadwood Dick.

Usefully engaged on a stool was the girl friend. Feeding to the fox by her on the fox fur-piece from a bowl on the bar, salted peanuts. One by a time yet. In between the peanuts, to the bartender she made orders.

"A double Scotch, Mohandas, and why on the radio can't we getting a swing band, a good hot one?"

Explanations made the bartender.

"On the radio is speaking in five minutes the President!"

What it made the blonde responses.

"In this case, you'll making it a triple Scotch."

"Yippee!" came wild cheers from the direction from the Pin Ball machine. "A special when lit!"

"You've been lit for years," gave snarls the blonde, "and there's nothing special about you."

"You see!" gave Phoebe to Fenimore a nudge.

18

Against the bar it leaned two pleasant worthwhile gentlemen. One with a nose, a freshly taped-up one. Deeply they worked out from a engineering nature, a problem. How to make from the end from a fork, a lump sugar it should fly into a glass beer.

With the nose to the grindstone was artistically occupied a policeman, painting by a poster from a gorgeous brunette, on the face a moustache.

And by a little table en route to the Cafe kitchen, stood the proprietor, Felix. Putting on a eclair, a chocolate one, finishing touches.

Surrounded was Felix by his pupil and assistant, Seymour. Nine years old was Seymour, with a bum liver already from overworry. A production was creating Felix with the eclair! First was chocolate, double layers. On the chocolate, yellow icing. On the icing, cherry glaces. On the glaces, lemon frosting. On the frosting, maraschinos! Paused Felix now with problems. What to putting on the top? To which it made suggestions Seymour.

"A Solarium . . . . or better still, tear it all down, and put up bungalows!"

The lunch, in between time was enjoying extremely Mister Figgits.

"Is positively irrespressible here the food my dear, is no?" he chirped to Phoebe. "Improofments, latest ones, they got here special. In the icebox they keep frozen, quails with peasants. In the abbatoir they keeping lobsters. . . . ."

"And in the drinking glasses, turtles," gave rejoiners Missus Figgits.

"Darling," made expostulations Mister Figgits, "Don't let it upset you that crackpot by the soap-box with the bomb. Hm, he upsets you . . . . he upsets me . . . . a jerk like this could upset

"Is positively irrepressible here the food!"

anybody. Pfooey . . . . bombs . . . . destruction. Pfooey!"

Behind him now stood Felix, waiting a opportune moment he should assail him with the eclair.

"For goodness sakes," gave answers Phoebe, "couldn't you talking from something else besides the bomb?"

"Okay my sweets! You naming him. The weather maybe in California, you would like to disgusting?"

"So what's with the weather wrong in California?" demanded Missus Figgits.

"So, what's wrong with the weather in California?"

"Who said was wrong?" gave assents Mister Figgits, "Is wonderful! My Uncle Pluto is loitering now in South Pasadena, what he writes it's so gorgeous there the weather, that the first day he threw away the umbrella; the second, the galoshes; the third, the raincoat; and if it wouldn't spilled on him on the fourth day, a wash boiler from water, he would still be perfectly dry! Hm, Bombs! Alarmists! The typewriting they see on every wall! Mark my words, my dear! Nothing is going to destroy the world!"

While behind him is still standing Felix with the eclair.

"But the bomb — it could be dangerous," made protests Phoebe. While tentatively to Mister Figgits it made Felix overtures:

"You eclair, sir!"

"They know what goes on . . . . they not so dumb . . . . they not asleep!" continued Mister Figgits.

"Who's they?"

"Who's they, she asks"! repeated Mister Figgits. "They the big boys . . . . The ones what running things. Jeepers creepers, dear, you think it runs things by themselves?"

"Frankly yes, at times!"

"Heh. Geopolitics, my dear, is something you should . . . . yes yes, my man?"

"You eclair, sir!"

"Please! go away! . . . . Now fundamentally, my love, in the general scheme from things, society plays two important . . . . Good grief, fellow! Stop breathing by me down the neck!"

"But, sir! You ecla. . . . ."

"Not now. As I was saying dear. . . . ."

"Better eat by him already the eclair. It's. . . . ."

"Please, dear! Fundamentally. . . . ."

"But suppose a enemy hides in one country a bomb. Suppose this country hides by the enemy a bomb. Suppose all at the same time. . . . ."

"Don't ask so many suppository questions. Learn better a little political economy. Now in political econ . . . . good grief, fellow, stop hanging by me on the ear. . . . ."

"But you eclair. . . . ."

"Take it away."

"Oh eat his eclair!"

"Why should I eat his eclair?

"He's standing too long on his feet. It's not good to stand too long on one's feet!"

"So let him stand on his ear! Good heavens, woman. One minute you worrying it'll blow up the world, and the next you worrying about his feet! Now in geopol. . . . ."

"Will it hurt you to eat his eclair?"

"But if I don't feel like to eat a eclair. . . . ."

"Just to-day you got to don't feel. Deliberately to make here scenes . . . . to embarrass me. It's staring at us already people. . . . ."

"But if I don't feel like eating a eclair, I don't feel like eating a eclair."

"Just to-day you don't feel. Every day so far you do feel. Why just to-day you. . . . ."

"The lady . . . . she is right, sir. . . . . Every day you. . . . ."

"And every year it flies the swallows back to Capistrano! So suppose one year they decide to fly back to Cuccamonga? Is by you okay?"

Happily it gave a dawn a light on Felix: "Ah! You desire a change I see now! So instead from a eclair, let me I should bring for you a tart!"

"Sure," gave assents Phoebe, "eclairs . . . . tarts . . . . anything. Just so he should eat it, we should get out from here. . . . ."

"Involved here," shouted Mister Figgits firmly, "is a question bigger from a eclair or a tart. Bigger from any tart in the joint!"

"I'll have you know I'm a lady, you fat sloppy punk!" gave screams the blonde with the fox fur, leaping off her stool. While sparring off in front from Mister Figgits is her drunken boy friend.

25

"It's bigger than any tart in the joint!"

"Eat it for the love of Mike!" gave loud a outburst Phoebe. "Eat his goddam eclair . . . . and lets. . . . ."

"If I don't feel like to eat it, why should I eat it? And what'll happen pray, if I don't eat it?"

"If you do not eat him," gave wailings Felix, "I am sad. I am desolate! When I am desolate I am nervous; and when I am nervous I cannot work; when I cannot work I lay in bed; and when I lay in bed the maid she will not clean the house. So you see. . . . ."

"All I see," roared Mister Figgits, "is that I ain't eating no eclair!"

"Pipe down, slob," came from the bar suggestions.

"Oh, yeah! How you'd like. . . . ."

"For the last time Fenimore Figgits. . . . ."

"For the last time, no! Involved here is fundamentals. . . . ."

"Involved is getting the whole joint! Fundamentals! Bombs! Geopolitics!—a blinking whole encyclopedia you became! Why don't it split you up someone in twenty volumes and give you away free with a set Boccachio?"

"Ha ha ha!" gave gales from laughter, from the bar, a raucous gentleman. "On me this calls for a snort, Babe! Hop up here on Papa's lap!"

"You'd like maybe a biff by the snoot, Brother?" made bristlings Mister Figgits.

"Sit down!" gave Missus Figgits screams. While by the coattails vainly she tried to grab him. All over the Cafe became inwiggled in the melee patrons. All but the cop, who begged please, he should be left out from it.

Advice to Phoebe offered the soused gent that characters like Mister Figgits should never in the first place drink.

"I resent this aspiration!" made protest Mister Figgits.

"Okay, then walk this chalk line pal . . . . this straight one!"

While suggestions made the blonde to throw the fat punk out. . . . .

"I defy you . . . . walk this straight line!"

Screaming now in uproars is the whole Cafe. Above the din is making Mister Figgits pleadings, "Don't you people realizing what's going on to-day? Don't it read anybody here the papers ever?"

"Sure," came from the bar razzberries, "It's in a awful mix-up. Little Mary Mix-up! Scram, bum!"

Baffled makes a gentleman inquiries: what could causing people like Mister Figgits to go around a whole time starting trouble?

To which significantly makes replies the bar-fly with the taped up nose. "A dame, pal. Always it's a dame!"

Gallantly above the din, roars Mister Figgits, "You'll leaving please my wife's name out from this!"

"Who said it was your wife, pal. I said a dame!"

"What did he meant by that crack?" gave Phoebe screams at Fenimore.

"Who knows . . . . a stew!"

"Oh no you don't, you heel. I saw him wink."

"Please let's go! We late for Monkey Island, dear, to visit there the monkeys!"

"I'll monkey you," made screeches Missus Figgits. "Over my dead body will we go." To which made chimings in the blonde; "A excellence idea!"

"You must eat my eclair!" gave wailings loudly Felix. With a flying hat-rack he was silenced!

Hair is now pulling with bites with kicks with scratchings. A free-for-all becomes the Cafe. To Mister Figgits makes the raucous gent suggestions, "Beat it jerk, before I smear the eclair all over your puss. . . . ."

"It happens to be two schools from thought on this preposition, brother . . . . Yours with mine. . . . ."

Screaming now in uproars is the whole Cafe.

29

"It's a dame . . . . always it's a dame!"

A poke the gentleman gives him with the eclair in the face. Biffs returns him Mister Figgits. Off the stools comes sailing patrons. From the bar comes bouncing bottles. From the window flies the watermelon—with the Battle from Gettysburg carved on it yet. In the face gets Missus Figgits, Pickett's Charge! Bottles, tables, mirrors . . . . Splinters! Like mad is fighting everybody. All but the cop, who is pleading he should be left out from it.

30

"I beg you . . . . please leave me out from this!"

Cuckoo it knocks him a flying pin-ball machine.

A shambles is the Cafe. Filled is the air with riot calls with sirens screaming.

And outside on the soap box is still proclaiming the orator.....

"Beware from the Atomic Bomb! A terrible force from detruction. Beware!"

"I beg you ... please leave me out from this!"

2

ARRANGED it stands Mister Figgits in The Night Court. Insighting riots is the charge. Bewilted with puzzled, he ponders. How from a clear sky out, to him, Fenimore Figgits, such a thing should happen.

A gentleman he is, a mild one. Respectable at all times, with law-abiding. Taxes he pays always on time. Crunchy candy bars he never chews loudly in theatres. In each can, by him in front from the house is always correctly placed the different styles garbage. Pedestrian lanes he always walks in. And the roller towel in the washroom, he never pulls out more from one at a time.

So now, just because he didn't eat a eclair, in the dock he's standing. Alienated is from him almost his adored wife, Phoebe. With trapadition, he is scrutinizing the Judge—and with a eye like a eagle, and a nose like a beagle, is scrutinizing the Judge, the charges.

Not too good, feels Mister Figgits. Then begins to speak the Judge:

"Hm . . . . let's we should see. From a flying pin-ball machine, a cop a broken jaw got?? . . . . Hm! Well, people only human after all! Could happen by you . . . . could happen by me. A mirror a smashed one, and by the bartender, five stitches in the scallop, with conclusion from the brain? Mm. . . . . Happens,

33

happens! Let's see . . . . a bus boy with a split personality, due to a flying fire-axe? . . . . No doubt is for it a reason. . . . . We must considering here all angles. . . . . A lady with a broken leg, and stabbed with a ice-pick a waiter? . . . . Let us not we should be hasty, with prune to leap by a conclusion. We are but children, all from us, humble, groping, straying, praying we should having light in connection with guidance. No doubt it has Mister Figgits a reasonable explanation for all this. . . . . It awaits the Court from Mister Figgits the pleasure. . . . ."

At a loss for words is Mister Figgits. Aback he is taken on account so mild with understanding is His Honor. Speechless he remains. And into the breach steps hastily Missus Figgits, to save for Fenimore the night.

"If it's pleasing You Honor," she vouchsafes tremulously a defense. "I think it's due the strange behavior on the part from my husband to some kind from a diet he is on!"

"A diet? . . . ." slowly repeated His Honor, while into his eye materialized a gleam, a omnibus one, and it underwent his whole mannerism a complete transfusion. "Did you said a diet?"

"My diet," began Mister Figgits, "has nothing to. . . . ."

"Silence!" gave a roar the Judge, who, unbeknownst to Mister with Missus Figgits, possessed a wife, a fat one from three hundred pounds, who for twenty years was each week on a different diet.

"So! Diets, ha! Well, well, my fat friend! Diets you on, ha? Come closer a little, we should have on you a good look! I know you breed, quite well, my rotund glutton! You do consist from a glutton, is no? . . . . Like a pig you stuffing yourself full, ha? You do stuffing, do you not? . . . . Quiet slob! You stuffing, ha, and then in front from the mirror a whole time you scream you are getting fat! Is no, Missus Figgits? From you diets, pig, you driving with your torments out from their minds, the poor victims the helpless ones, who got to live with you. . . . . Do I'm right? Cranky with crotchety rages, with tantrums you getting

34

from you self-inflected martyrdom. . . . . ha. Don't telling me, I know! And then on you poor wife you venting it all. Do I'm right Missus Figgits? Round like a barrel you guzzling, and on the family you taking it out. Do I'm unerring? Oh, how well I know you type, you beast with bully with tyrant. Is no Missus

"You are a fat slob, aren't you!"

Figgits? If it comes three minutes late to the theatre, your wife, so you'll tear up in pieces the tickets, ha? Is no? Answer me, Madam. Did you or did you was ever by a theatre late. . . . . Answer, before I holding you in content from Court. Did you or did you was ever late?"

"W-w-well, y-y--es, I w-was."

"So I right, ha? Tickets he tears up! Chairs he smashes. Dogs he kicks, I'll bet. On the tiptoes it's got to creep the whole house if by his Majesty is tuned on the radio, ha? Company you couldn't have on account a whole night he's insulting them! Hours he'll sulk if it ain't ready on the minute dinner. Then a meal he gobbles, what from a boa-constructor it would bust the seams. And with the feet on the table a whole night he'll snore, ha? A bully . . . . a tyrant . . . . a monster. . . . . Smoke he blows into the goldfish bowl. The kind from a man what paints knotholes on iron telephone poles; it should break the poor wood-peckers the bills, ha? . . . . Yes or no? Well, answer me my fat slob. Do you or do you not paint . . . . knotholes."

What for a answer it gave a jump at the Judge Mister Figgits, like a mongoose to tearing in pieces a kober. Unable was almost two bailiffs with a traffic cop to overpowder him from the ber-serkness. And remarks it made His Honor:

"To this we'll adding charges from a salt with battery. In front from a Jury you'll having a trial. Adjoined is the Court!"

Dragged away was Mister Figgits. Screaming tearfully was Phœbe.

A turn on, in his chambers it gave His Honor the Radio. Out came poetry, so:

> *Great wide beautiful wonderful world!*
> *With the wonderful water around you curled;*
> *With the wonderful grass by you on the breast;*
> *World you are wonderfully dressed!*

Snorts gave His Honor:

"From the fifth from Hialeah, I wanting the returns, and fashion styles I'm getting by this rat trap! Bah!"

A stalk he gave out from the Court. Two bucks he borrowed from the Bailiff for a snifter. A kick in the face he gave "One-legged Pete," the old pencil peddler. A cab he grabbed for the Tosso El Torso Club. But first a phone call he stopped to make to a boom companion with old friend, Admiral Frisbee. It should dine with him on the morrow the Admiral; he should be a alibi in case it decided His Honor to decapitating his wife.

On the streets played joyously from Hurty-Gerties, maladies.

God's in his Heaven, Mister Figgits in Jail.

Rompling on the walks was little children. Sex with hatchet murders, with Marcel Proust they playfully discussed. Golden set the sun. And in the Park, it gave a pass Pippa Pipkin with poetic idles, so:

> *By larks it is wings*
> *By butterflys also;*
> *By hornets is stings,*
> *What they creep on the wall so.*
> *Pearls from dew by the hillside,*
> *In the thorn is a snail;*
> *God's in his Heaven,*
> *Mister Figgits in Jail.*

Into the Jury room it marched from Mr. Figgits trial the Jury, to put together their heads. Which all twelve at once could fit

Into the Jury room marched the Jury.

under a six-with-three-eighths hat. Looks it gave the Foreman by the three members from the Jury what belonged in the category from females. Decisions he made—that to be locked up with them in a hotel overnight shouldn't happen to a dog.

So the ball he started rolling so:

"He's guilty like anything, boys with girls. So what for should we sojurn here in a musty room . . . . subversively making from valuable time expendures, effete with barren with sterile? . . . . Misused with squandered, a forfiture, a total dissipation? Let's better give the bum quick the works, and get home. Okay, we'll vote. All in favor from guilty will pronouncing 'Aye!'"

So out it came eleven times, "ayes," but by the twelfth time, instead from a "aye," it came out a "no!"

Aside it stepped the Jury. From the middle from it, materialized a individual a short one, who defiantly made repititions:

"No!"

By the Foreman gave a arch significantly the eyebrow. "Once more we'll trying this," he made announcements, "with no funny business!"

What again emerged eleven "ayes," with one "no!" So to the dissenter it addressed himself the Foreman so:

Again he repeated, "No!"

"If you'll excuse me very much, Mister Justice Oliver Wendell Holmes. I would like to asking, just whom do you think you consist from?"

Replies made the dissenter: "Juror Number Twelve. Don't you remember? I passed you during lunch the ketchup!"

"Look brother, we dont want trouble here with you!"

"A ringer, ha! Stooge for the mouthpiece," came from the rest yells. "How much his lawyer pays you, ha? A pal from the culprit, eh. . . . . Well, with trouble-makers like Figgits, we making short shrift kid. . . . ."

Remonstrations made Juror Number Twelve:

"Gentlemen, I never before in all my life, laid upon Mister Figgits, eyes."

"Quiet, muzzler! Who did you paid off to getting back you fingerprints? By a jury fixer you on the payroll, maybe? With the culprit you was gradually in San Quentin by the Juke Mill partners, ha? Come clean grifter. A racket you got here a good one, is no?"

"Gentlemen, gentlemen. Rackets I aint looking for. Never in all my life did I ever served before by a Jury. On this one, even I didn't wished to serve. . . . ."

"Oho. . . . . Didn't wished to serving by a Jury, ha. Anti-social with a Bolshevik yet, is no? Too hoity-toity maybe for the likes from us, eh?"

"But now, that I do here, I strongly desiring we should doing the right thing. Irregardless it takes a little longer the job!"

"Looks pretty good to you that three bucks a day, ha, chiseler?"

"Gentlemen, I make on my job six bucks a day!"

"A stinking capitalist! Also laying down on you boss! Working here a racket. Pretty soft a touch, a sweet one ha? Stretching out with meals with hotels yet. . . . . Look pal, you couldn't win. So give gradually a vote guilty, and let's we should getting the hell out from here. It's got my wife simpering home on the oven a roast, a black-market one!"

"Gentlemen," gave responses Juror Number Twelve, "Mister Figgits refused he should eating a eclair. Under the Magna Carta, it has Mister Figgits the right not to eating a eclair!"

"You'd like maybe a paste in the eye?" made inquiries Juror Number Four.

"Quiet, Snackery," made admonitions the Foreman. "This we doing strictly according by procedure! Mister Figgits sought he should imposing his will in the Cafe on the majority. This is tantamount to a dictatorship. What he resorted yet to force with violence, insighting to riot in conjunction with intimidation!"

"But the evidence . . . ." expostulated Juror Number Twelve.

"Evidence, hah! None from you slick lawyer tricks! Who's needing evidence. Gimme good hard facts from a horse sense nature yet! Fore with violence we dont stand for here."

"You ketch? Okay. So you in here on a rain check. Be gradually a good guy. . . . ."

"Don't waste time with the jerk!" it interloped Juror Number Two.

"Quiet, Potpecker!" made admonitions the Foreman.

"Wrap him a chair around the neck!" suggested Juror Number Three, a lady.

"By no means Missus Rasselass!" gave replies the Foreman. "Via logic we seeking to convincing Mister . . . . Mister . . . . by the way, what's by you the name, pal?"

"Smith. John Smith."

"Smith, ha! Well, well. Small world!"

"And getting smaller!"

"Ha ha. You sure got a lot buttoned up in them few words, Smitty. Mm. . . . . Gradually not a bad Joe, boys! By the way Smitty, this is Missus Rasselass. Potpecker, you already know. Over there is Keewis, Ishkadoo, Snackery, with Hodge, Boggleweiss, Gazzwatts, Ding, and Tranifatts. Now Smitty, you here in town a citizen. All our privileges you enjoining, is no? Candy bars by theatres. Free Parking by the Market. Red with green lights by traffic stops. Socially you gravitate to dances, parties, balls, is no? So how it'll gonna look, you should making on the ballroom floor, with you wife a entrance. You do got a wife, don't you?"

"I do."

"So with you wife you coming down the ballroom the grand staircase. Beautiful she's gowned with gorgeous. The sinecure from all eyes. Dapper with sharp are you! A handsome couple. So how it's gonna look when it exclaims everybody, 'Now what could it have happened, to Mister Smith's left ear? It was on there only yesterday!' You ketch, Smitty? So how you voting? Guilty

41

"*We don't stand for violence with intimidation here, pal!*"

or not guilty?"

"Not guilty!"

"Hmmmm! You got maybe a cigar, Keewis?"

"You wish to bribing the jerk?"

"Who said from bribing? Gimme a match. Toss him on the table, boys. Rip him off the shoes with sox. Seems it needs our Mister Smith convincings. That we don't tolerating in this town force with violence. Light up, Potpecker. Well, Smitty . . . . how you voting?

"Not guil . . . . OUCH!"

"How? . . . . Sorry, I didn't heard you. I a little nostalgic in one ear to-day. Try again . . . . Louder. . . . . Aha! Good! You a man from public spirit, with a civet-minded sense from duty. Kibosh County has made its answer. No room do we got in our fair community for force with violence; browbeating with intimidation. Figgits is guilty!"

3

Aᴛ ʜɪs ᴅᴇsᴋ, a gorgeous with ornate one yet, sat Mister Sizwell Fizwell. Chairman from the Board he was, from a gigantic corporation entitled Fizwell, Wizwell, with Philpot—Investments. Also was Mister Fizwell the employer from Fenimore Figgits. Who for twenty years was by Fizwell Wizwell with Philpot, the confidential clerk with bookkeeper.

Via the telephone at the moment it was undergoing Mister Fizwell with his wife a conversation. Jubiliously she made to him

announcements that by them in the house had just arrived a new maid.

Down made a dive Mister Fizwell to the barber shop.

Conjectures he was making from the new maid.

Tall with slinky.

Blonde? brunette?
A piperoo—a slickchick!

Short with sweet.

46

Till it aroused him from the revelry the barber with a state-
ment: "I now pronounce you shaved!"

Snazzy, sniftious, slinky, spiff splendacious!

Home rushed gaily Mister Fizwell.

A ring he gave the bell. A opening gave the door. . . . . So, instead from a slick-chick piperoo, slinky with snazzy with splendacious, is greeting him in a maid's uniform a ape!

So it greeted him instead a ape entitled Ingrid!

Fainting spells had almost Mister Fizwell. To the spouse a gasp he gave:

"What do you calling this?"

Responses sweetly made the spouse,

"Ingrid!"

While coyly with shy it gazed adoringly on Mister Fizwell, Ingrid, and made demurely to him a courtesy with her finger in the chin.

Explanations from the phenomenon, demanded weakly Mister Fizwell. What it replied him the spouse.

"You realize my dear, the shortage from domestic help these days very cricketal indeed. So, in order to alienating this, it's

Coyly made a courtesy Ingrid.

training now a Domestic Help Institute, apes, they should doing housework.

"And you of course had to heard from it."

"From Missus Blatt . . . . She heard it last week by a Salon. So quick she telephoned to Mister Blatt, the glad tidings. Also orders he should bringing home a ape.

So, on the way from the office, stops Mister Blatt by a Apiary, to making inquiries. Apiaries yet, heh, heh. Such ignorance people. Lumps with stings he comes out with. On account . . . . heh, heh. . . . . You know dearest, a Apiary is strictly for bees a rendevous. Apes you obtain elsewhere.

"So direct from the Institute I acquired Ingrid. You should see from rafters now is dusted cobwebs! A pleasure with a joy is housework. Except one thing. She's afraid from grunions. They remind her from snakes. So the grunions I'll have to fry myself. But is only two days a year. So is okay!" . . . . .

But none of this heard Mister Fizwell. On account, he already gave with his study a stalk with a slam yet by the door, that in the University from Cape Town it registered yet on the seismograph a earthquake!

So in order it should be made convertible the ape language into English, it supplied the Domestic Institute to all apes, a United Nations language converter.

This converter they using in case it wishes by a United Nations meeting, gentleman from Siam to addressing maybe to the gentleman from Uruguay, a speech. So in Siamese, he makes into the converter on one end a speech. And out from the other end it comes the speech in Uruguanian.

So into the converter, it made Ingrid speeches.

"Abba wabba dabba babba."

And out from it came language so:

"You didn't heard, dearie, the latest stink. . . . . So, wait, I'll spilling you! My boss . . . . poor Mister Fizwell. . . . . So adorable he looks yet in a yellow dressing gown. Romantic with dignified. I love a man a little gray by the temples . . . . don't you? What he could seeing in that battle-axe from a Missus Fizwell, I couldn't imagining! Of course, I only a ape. But irregardless, it's got now poor Mister Fizwell such troubles. With sympathy I overpowdered. All on account, it's working by him in the office a dope, a stupe, a tack-headed blubberbrain, a mope, entitled Fenimore Figgits."

"How could it make for him in the office a mope trouble?"

"He didn't ate a eclair!"

"He didn't ate a eclair?"

"And you should see, how it's now in a hot corner as a result from this Fizwell, Wizwell, with Philpot!"

"Because Figgits didn't ate a eclair, it's in a jam, his bosses?"

"Headache powers they chewing up all morning like peanuts, dearie! Yeh, upstairs they all are now in the library. Philpot is the one with the dishpan covering his head. Dishpans he's got to sticking over the head, on account I don't liking by him the

A pleasure is now housework!

face. It insists on it Missus Fizwell, in order I shouldn' quitting. They sure catering here to me, the dopes!"

"So, if it didn't eat Mister Figgits a eclair," interrupted Begonia, "why should it be by them such a sauce from irrigation?"

"Hm. . . . . Riots, fights with scandals with Night Courts, emanated from it."

"Then pure with simple, they should firing the dope!"

She's afraid from grunions!

"This, is a monopulation, dearie, in which is inwiggled a good deal more than is meeting the eye. . . . . Poor Mister Fizwell. Carmine pajamas he also looks gorgeous in."

"You mean is mixed up in the whole thing some kind from skulldrudgery?"

"You got a very scientific mind, dearie! So long what you smelling the rat, I'll tipping you off all the lowdown. But cross you heart. Under the bonnet. Strictly ontray noose."

Over the fence it gave a gossip Ingrid!

"Who do I see? I live up in the Canyon. Give sister."

"So wait. Behind the fancy front scenery is carrying on Fizwell, Wizwell, with Philpot a business . . . . don't esk. Hankypanky deals they pulling. Tricks they knowing all the fast ones. Fronts with cover-ups they needing. So who could be a better dummy than Mister Figgits?"

"So what is a dummy?"

"A patsy with a fall guy. To covering up when they put by him in the name all kinds stocks with bonds, with cash with assets, which is really belonging to the boss. You ketch?"

"I got it all salted down hours ago sister. No wonder it's having puppies, Fizwell, Wizwell, with Philpot. How much from their assets is in dopey Figgits' name?"

"A million dollars! What could sue him now a cop for a jaw, a broken one. A proprietor for a Cafe a wrecked one. And a hospital full from innocent banisters for damages, physical ones."

"Yi yi yi yi yi yi!"

"So wait dearie! Don't going away! I'll give quick a shinny up the drainpipe. A eavedrop I'll making by the Library on the conference. And the latest bulletin, I'll waylaying to you."

Up the pipe it gave a shinny, Ingrid.

Into the Library, with a vacuum cleaner, in order it should be a subterfudge, she wafted. Up against the wall was backed in

Eavesdrops then made Ingrid!

desperation Philpot . . . . still with the dishpan over the face. Roaring on him with cursory language, with oats terrible ones, was Fizwell. To the roots from her fur, blushed Ingrid, and a shinny down the drain-pipe, she gave back to Begonia.

"This'll gonna kill you dearie. I only a ape . . . . but, such dopes I'm meeting already among people, that in Borneo, they couldn't get into a class in a monkey kindergarten, where it weaves morons baskets. Wait yet. Business technicalities I just learning. When you put something in a dummy's name, you get first a release on paper! In case it happens something to the dummy. Then with the paper, you get back the dough.

"A dummy you should only get who you can trust. Who could Fizwell, Wizwell, with Philpot trust more than Mister Figgits? In fact, they trusted him so much, that dopey Philpot trusted him to put away the paper in the safe. Ha ha! So now all week they searching for the paper in the safe! And off their noodle they are going! On account is in the safe no paper! In the desks, with draws, with vaults, with chubbyholes . . . . no paper! Wait, more news in a minute, dearie!"

This time, epsom-mindedly Ingrid is with the garden hose, hosing in the library the rug. While with one ear, she is listening how it outlines a stragedy Mister Fizwell to Philpot. What is still by him the dishpan on the head! Schemes it outlines Mister Fizwell so:

"Well dope. Into this you got us, and out from it you'll also

This time with a garden hose the rug she hosed.

56

getting us. Home from a suspended sentence is eminently due any minute Figgits. If the three from us go to him to snag the missing paper, it will make suspicious the shrew, what he calls a wife. Such a calumnity would be to us approximately fatal. You, the one what you gave him the paper to put away. So you to him will go. Stragedy you'll employ! Tact with diplomacy you'll use! Oil you'll spread! Raises you'll promise for him. Flowers you'll bring for the shrew. Deftfully the paper you'll grab, and so soon you'll grab it, we'll kick him down the stairs. Back you should come with the paper, or on it . . . . Go. . . . ."

In a modern little frame house, it lived the Mister with the Missus Figgits. Modern with up to date, with post-war yet, what remarked often the Missus Figgits!

"We got everything but the kitchen sink."

To which made witticisms Mister Figgits!

"So we washing up by the spiggot in the garage!"

To which it made replies Missus Figgits to her dearest girl friend Ruthie, "You see what I mean, dearie!"

So by Missus Figgits it gave, the doorbell gradually a ring!

To the door, Missus Figgits wended her way. On account at the moment, she was painting in the attic the ceiling. A fling open she gave the door. Standing there was Philpot. In the hand a bouquet from orchids, and epsom-mindedly was over the face still the dishpan what he forgot on the trip to doffing it. What remarked the Missus Figgits.

"Well well! Give a look! The age from romance. Visits I get from the man in the Iron Mask! Is no wolf? Candlestine dates you trying to promote gradually, ha? Lose yourself, but quick!"

So inside from the dishpan it said to himself Philpot.

"Yi, yi! Is a lucky thing I got over my head the pan. A lucky thing she didn't recognizing me. On I will keep it, and excuses I will make for the call, any kind. Then craftily I'll return later in my true guise, and warily, I'll inwiggle away from Figgits the paper."

So to the Missus Figgits, he made declamations so:

"I beg you pardon fair lady. Intrusions I didn't meant to wreaking upon you by the privacy. But it just so happens, I ran out

"Give a look the man in the Iron Mask! Scram bum!"

from matches. You could see here in my hand a cigar, a unignited one . . . . and I thought maybe. . . . ."

"Keep moving wise guy. . . . ."

"My dear lady, it protested Philpot forgetting from the mission his object! I beg by you the pardon, but at high noon, I not in the habit from going on the make. Especial for a dame accountered in her old man's overalls, and covered all over on her shiny nose with paint. . . . . I told you I ran out from matches!"

"Two seconds I'll give you to get out from here before I slop by you this paint brush all over the puss."

"If you do sister," it assured her Philpot, I'll guarantee you, I'll running the handle . . . . oops."

Up the street it ran in a panic Philpot on account in this moment it flew out from him from the pocket inadvertently, a pack matches. What for a half a block up, was banging him on the dishpan with the paint brush Missus Figgits. . . . .

Back in the little frame house was waiting for her the dearest girl friend Ruthie. To Ruthie it gave now outpourings Missus Figgits. . . . .

"You see, dearie. Wolves, wolves, wolves! Every one from them. . . . ."

What gave responses Ruthie.

"Take my word for it, dearie. They all a pack from dogs. Every last one, including my Clarence, with your Fenimore."

"My Fenimore?"

"All men are dogs, believe me!"

"Around the corner I wouldn't trust the best from them. The longer they married, the more they on the sneak. Not for nothing did it made cracks, that guy in the Cafe. 'It's a dame!' Oh yes, don't looking dearie, so shocked. Is always the wife the last to find out. Oh, they very subtile all right. The whole lowdown pack from chippie chasers. Hm, leave it to them they should covering up the trackprints. . . . . Flowers for you by Mother's Day. Boxes candy it should be five times a week surprises. Telephone calls, dutiful ones, in the middle from the morning, what it wouldn't melt by them butter in the mouth. Lambie love, with honey cuddle yet! And the dope wife is from the whole neighborhood the laugh stocking . . . . Take my word, dearie, the last one on earth, I'd be to breathing a word . . . . but where is smoke must be fire. Well, good-bye lovey. Got to running. . . . ."

From the back door it gave a departure Ruthie, and toward the front door, it made approaches Mister Figgits, released he freshly was from jail. In the hand, a bunch flowers, and for the Missus Figgits greetings which he was rehearsing so:

"Lambie love with honey cuddle mine! For your fair tresses, flowers from a tulip nature, and for your sweet lips from Papa kisses. Finished is with the eclair all the silly business. Hatchets we will bury! Bygones will be bygones. Home is Papa to the hearth, the fireside, the pipe, the slippers, the little woman. . . . ."

Open flew the door, and out like a rocket into the street was jet-propelled Mister Figgits. Past the fence, on top from the lawn across the street, through a bus, and into a tree. What from the branches fell out apples, dunt esk! That if it was sleeping under the tree, Sir Issac Newton, so instead from laws from gravitation, he would write instead a song, Don't Sit Under The Apple Tree . . . . period!

Following the apples, it fell out from the tree, Mister Figgits. Away he walked . . . . and walked. . . . .

Wandering around, befuddled . . . . in a daze. With deep perplexion he is trying to figure out, from people the heartlessness.

Home from Jail came Mister Figgits.

Sympathy with understanding he yearns for from his wife. Kicks in the face out through the door he gets instead.

Sorely is puzzled poor Mister Figgits. Sore in the seat, and puzzled in the head. Scandals he is now accused from. On account, all over the neighborhood, it spilled Phoebe's dearest girl friend Ruthie, all the dirt. Friends, when now he passes, give quick in doorways jumps. Neighbors shunt him, and acquaintances pull in from sidewalks little children when he passes. What to himself it spoke Mister Figgits.

"Do I'm contanimated? Do I'm a Uriah? Should I maybe tie around me by the neck a bell I should walking down the street, it should ring, I should give yells, 'Unclean?' All on account I forewent a eclair?"

What from a ash barrel gave a response a voice:

"I passed up in Omaha once a hamburger, pal. . . . . . It's murder!"

All over town is drifting Mister Figgits from pillow to post.

And out the door went flying.

Efforts he is making wild goose ones to get sympathy! Strangers he is buttonholing on the street to help him understand by human people the inconsistencies. Razzberries he is getting with threats to call a cop. Also promissory assurances that if he don't lose himself, but fast, so from a bucket garbage he'll get a shower.

Gradually to a barroom, a lowdown one he finds his way. On his chin it sprouts now stubbles. Baggy is his clothes with crumpled. Under one ear is his necktie. A double snort he is inhaling, and addresses he is making to the gentry in the joint:

"I didn't ate a eclair!"

"Ulcers?" made cheerfully inquiries a party with a patch by one eye. While admonitions it made to him a seafaring personality:

"Quiet, Bow-wow. Don't interrupt when it's buying us the gentleman a round champagne!"

"As I was saying," began again Mister Figgits.

Strangers he is buttonholing on the streets!

"This time, all around mint juleps! Your very good health sir. A pleasure to imbibe with a gentleman like you a julep. Bottoms aloft!"

"I didn't eat a eclair!"

"You didn't eat a eclair? . . . . beer this time, barman! All around—your health sir!"

"Sometimes a man don't want to eat a eclair! He's got a right! Could be a day he just don't feel like it. So if he don't want to eat a eclair, he don't want to eat a eclair!"

"You hear, Rusty. Among us comes a man from vast ideas. He don't want to eat a eclair, so he don't want to eat a eclair! Socrates!"

"Don't interrupt the gentleman, Hot-rod! Especial when he's trying to persuade us all around to fill them up again. Zombies, barman!"

"So where did it was this eclair," inquired the bartender with a wink, while in the same time he is making with the finger by the forehead circles.

"Let him tell it his own way, Mack. Like it told from North Carolina the Governor to South Carolina . . . . Ale with stout all around! You insist, pal? So is okay! Fill 'em up, Mack. Ale with stout all around. Is by the gentleman the pleasure!"

"It was on a plate, of course," gave explanations Mister Figgits, slightfully sardonic, what he added, "It didn't was on the top from the Washington Monument!"

"Ha ha ha!" gave guffaws loudly Bow-wow, "You slay me pal. Make it all around now side-cars! . . . . And let the gentleman he should tell his story. But first, another round old fashioneds!"

"I consist from a victim," began Mister Figgits, "a victim from the world we living in."

"Tell us about it, pal. And sparkling Burgundy, all around." "What's the use I should tell you, friend" gave answers Mister Figgits, "Take for yourself a look! Look out from any window. Or worse even yet look into any window. From the housetops go yet shout it . . . . except who's got a house? To your wife try you should tell it . . . . hah! Try, yet she should see it. . . . ."

"Wifes couldn't seeing nothing," made sagely comments Bow-wow, "unless it's by you a blonde hair on the coat lapel. Or hidden by you a two-dollar bill in the left shoe."

"This I don't go all the way along with," gave responses, Mister Figgits. "Of course in some way my wife is slightly a shrew, but. . . . ."

"What ways?" gave interruptions Hot-rod. "Tell me kid! Maybe I'll discover one I didn't bumped into yet."

"Clearly," gave interruptions Bow-wow, "it's suffering our friend here from wife trouble. . . . ."

"A good Joe he seems to be too," made comments Lumpy. "So slip us the broad's address, pal. We'll take care from her."

"Sure," made chimings in Hot-rod. "Five dollars for a broken leg with a crowbar, is by us the usual rates. . . . . But you a good

64

"I'm a victim from the world we live in!"

Joe. so it's on us the deal. . . . ."

"Gentlemen, gentlemen!" gave gasps from horror Mister Figgits. "This is just the whole crust from the problem. With breaking legs with crowbars, we don't settle things. It ain't my wife
the fault . . . . It ain't me. It ain't Felix. It ain't the Jury, it ain't
the Judge. It's people . . . . they blind . . . . they dumb. . . . . Oh,
if I could only get one person in the world should understand
me"

"Okay," said Bow-wow. "It dont appeal to you a crowbar?
So instead we'll toss her down a flight from cellar steps. This way
for the same price you might hit a jackpot. Could be maybe two
broken legs, with a neck dislocated!"

"Quiet, Bow-wow!" gave yells Lumpy, "Don't you see it's
desirous the gentlemen to buy us another round?"

"I getting so riled up," continued Mister Figgits, "I getting so

riled up I . . . . another round, you said, gentlemen? Heheh! . . . .
I would love to oblige . . . . but it's run out gradually by me the
dough . . . . But I getting so riled up. I . . . . I. . . . ."

"Riled up you getting from conditions?" made inquiries the
bartender.

"Riled up I'm getting from conditions!"

"And dough you running out from?"

"This I must regretfully admit!"

"So for such a thing I got a sensational anticdote, my friend,"
replied the bartender. While in the same time he fingered significantly a bungstarter with a ice-pick. "What you needing is
a change!"

"Change? From what a change?"

"From scenery a change, my friend. To go away. It told me
once a high class gypsy that whenever I get riled up from conditions. . . . ."

"And run out at the same time from dough," chimed in Hot-
rod.

"Of course, Hot-rod! One without the other is no good. Any
dearest life-long friend could tell you this. So it told me this
gypsy, that under such a exigency, I should go away. Get gradually interested in new objects with surroundings!"

"Away? New objects with surroundings? Where?"

"Anywhere! Grab the first train marked 'Express!'"

"Or the first door marked 'Gents!' Heh."

What to the bungstarter with the ice-pick it now added the
bartender significantly a blackjack. And in the same time it
made to Mister Figgits the ensemblage warm with touching,
farewell going away speeches. . . . . "Your old lady had the itch.
Also you got a face like a cat's tail on a frosty morning . . . ."
with other similar endearing sentiments.

White with blanching it took his departure Mister Figgits.
Backwards he gave stumbles in his haste to leave. And into the
washroom through a wrong door gave a lurch.

"You remember . . . . you was there."

Failing to get interested in the new objects surrounding him, it swayed Mister Figgits gradually in front from the mirror by the wash-stand. Spinning is the walls around him. . . . . Dazed he is with sorely puzzled. . . . . Hurt with sensitive his feelings. So in the mirror to himself he commences to addressing speeches, so:

"Boy, is this a crummy stack-up! I ask you Fenimore, what it gives to-day with people? It didn't always was like this the world. I remember when I was a little boy . . . . walking down a country lane. . . . .

"You remember, you was there. . . . . And all from a sudden it appeared in my path a beetle. And I was just going to step on the beetle, when it whispered to me a voice:

'Don't step on that beetle'!

67

"And I didn't step on the beetle . . . . You was a witness. . . . .

"So it was good. I tried that I should do a little something, I should feel good, the beetle should feel good, maybe a little bit the whole world should feel good. So I did felt good, maybe it felt the beetle good, maybe it felt a little bit the whole world good. . . . . So it whispers me again the other day the voice:

'Don't eat that eclair.'

"And I didn't ate the eclair. I thought I should do again a little something it should be good. So dun't esk! . . . . A shambles it becomes a Cafe. Sneers I getting, with scoffs, with jeers. Centers from a ring from pointing fingers I become. I get avoided like a plague! Fines with jails, with lectures it hands me out a judge. Accusative incinerations from my wife I'm recipient from. All because I didn't ate a eclair. I could get so riled . . . . I could boil. Rancor inside from me blazes. Rage is taking from me possession. I could smite . . . . I could punch with blows. . . . ."

With his eyes closed, blind from rage with fury with anger, Mister Figgits gave such a punch in the side from a wooden panel, that splintered in pieces it became. Up to the elbow it crashed through his fist. Something hard inside it smacked against, with thuds dull ones. Transfixed stood Mister Figgits. What slowly swung, on the adjacent side from the panel, open the door from a booth. And out on his face it fell a gentleman, a unconscious one, what was adhering to him yet on the side from the face, busted pieces from the panel.

"Yi yi," gave exclamations Mister Figgits, "It seems what I conked a innocent by-sitter! Via the skylight I better lose myself but fast. Before from the bar comes in here the ensemblage."

Quick it gave Mister Figgits a shinny up the side from the booth. On the spiggots from the washbasin he gave a hop to reach the skylight. Off it broke the spiggots. Down he gave a slip into the basin. Pouring from the pipes is water. Footbaths

"I get so riled up, I get boiling!"

with the shoes on he is taking. And on the floor it gives the gentleman a stir, with suggestions to Mister Figgits, he should kindly explain things.

A clean breast it decided Mister Figgits to make.

"I didn't ate a eclair!"

Blinks it gave the gentleman with responses:

"You'll excuse by me extremely the curiosity, but I would be enormously obliged you should render me a synopsis, what it's got to do you not eating a eclair, with me winding up by a washroom floor knocked cold!"

A chronology commenced Mister Figgits from the whole affair.

While in between the meantime, over the back fence it was waylaying Ingrid to the maid from the house next door, the latest news from the dilenema from Fizwell Wizwell with Philpot:

"Hm . . . . an awkward situation."

"This'll kill you dearie! It's leaving now Mister Fizwell to take over where Philpot butched with Missus Figgits the deal!"

"Philpot butched the deal?"

"And how he butched it. Leary now is Missus Figgits. Unknown is still the hide-out from the paper. On the bum is Figgits missing. And lawsuits. . . . . Sh . . . . here is coming Mister Fizwell. Give a look! Dignified—romantic. A man what he has suffered! And wow! Does it send me, that perfume which he uses! Sh . . . . here he's coming. Tell me dearie . . . . do I'm blushing? Quick . . . . let's make out what we talking from something else." So it passed them Mister Fizwell, what in a loud voice said Ingrid to Begonia:

"It's a lie. Senator Cashew never did hide nuts by him in the jowls."

By the Missus Figgits to the front door, arrived gradually Mister Fizwell. In a fatherly manner, he is giving on the door

Epsom-minded she is trimming with a hedge clipper the drapes.

a knock. Benign he is putting himself in a mood to appear. On the face a look, a fake one, he establishes, it should denote grave concern. Open it gives a fling the door Missus Figgits, ready with a chromium pipe to conk Philpot again over the dome. So, instead from Philpot is standing on the doormat, Mister Fizwell. What from Phoebe emerges a squeak:

"Mister Fizwell!"

"My dear child! It came to us rumors that it is here annoying you through a hole in a dishpan a peeping Tom. Let me assuring you. . . . ."

"Oh Mister Fizwell . . . . give on me a look. I must be a sight. The vacuum I was just taking apart."

"You a sight? My child how dare could you breathe such a thing. A sweet-pea by a clinking vine from jassamine in a June noon. Oh but forgive me. I sometimes dappling in poetry. May I come in?"

"Do Mister Fizwell . . . . pray do! But the house . . . . it's something terrible a mess!"

"Look, she says a mess. My dear, dear child! How could you say even such a thing? A mess she's calling this adorable little house! My my! Dotted Swiss! Just like by my paternal grand-mamma in the ancestral home. And stain proof tops by you on all the tables. With a kitchen from a knotty pine! Pottery, no less on the open shelves. . . . . Yi, give a look! A ruffled frame on the mirror. I just simply adoring ruffled frames! Yourself you made him, is no? Just like I thought. How few it's handy to-day the young girls. . . . . My my. Horizon blue the walls. My favorite shade. . . . . But, look! What could this was? With the face turned backwards to the wall is hanging here a picture? Who could it was?"

"It's him! the rat!"

"Him? . . . . Rat? My dear little girl, who could him the rat consist from?"

"A no good wolf, a screwball, a jerk, a dope, a two-timing

72

chippy-chasing low down heel from a husband from mine. With who I'm through like anything!"

"My dear child! Come here. Sit by me. Hmm. . . . . Such soft hands, with a adorable complecture in the cheeks! So this is the little girl which it is hiding from us all these years, the selfish Mister Figgits. Naughty, naughty! Keeping all to himself so bewitching like you, a little creature!"

"Oh, Mister Fizwell!"

"Well, you a pretty cute trick, you know, babe. You with me kid could . . . . Yi yi . . . . but what do I'm saying? Forgive me, my dear. A play I was concocting. For the stage a play of course. Not the other kind from a play was I making . . . . heh heh. . . . ."

"Witty Mister Fizwell!"

"Lucky Mister Figgits!"

"He's a low-down, cheap. . . . ."

"Sh, my child! Evil to her who evil thinks. Married men don't go around a whole time on the make. How do you ever get into your pretty little head such ideas? Boy it sure brings out the blue in this slip, the blue from your eyes. But these foolish notions you must forget. Married men ain't wolves. This is all cheap newspaper talk with inaccurate surveys. Come here little one . . . . closer. Look me in the eye. Now tell me dear . . . . Why is it all the most sweet with charming girlies, all have husbands dopey ones who. . . . ."

"Oh, Mister Fizwell! How could you say such lovely things. Why you hardly knowing me!"

"Know you, my gorgeous little gazelle? All my life I have known you. Ever since I was first able at the age from four, to thrill to everything which is sweet with lovely, tender, shy with beautiful!"

"Oh . . . . *Mister Fizwell!!*"

"In the fragrance from a honeysuckle clinking by a vine in the summer sun, have I known you! In the song what it warples a lark on top from a meadow in June! When it paints with gold

73

"Oh! Mister Fizwell!!"

the sunset, and it gives a sigh with a kiss to the top of the mountain, a woodland breeze, have I known you! In everything what is young with fresh, with sweet with beautiful I have known you always!"

"Oh . . . . You think from such wonderful things to say, Mister Fizwell!"

"Tell me from you childhood, little one. You home. You family. From where did you came? A little town upstate, perchance?"

"How ever did you knew that Mister Fizwell?"

"And every morning it awakened you outside you window, the sweet song from the thrush! Or maybe from a woodland brook a gargle, what it passed you by the door?"

"Oh, no. Every morning it awakened us six-thirty prompt, from the Reformatory next door, the whistle. Out it would jump Papa then from bed. Two minutes would wait Mamma, while under the coffee pot it gave Papa a light the gas. Then out would jump Mamma. While into the bathroom, through the hall ran Uncle Joe. Into the kitchen would then run Mamma, via one door, and out from the kitchen, via the other door, it ran Papa back to the bedroom to dress. Two minutes loitered Uncle Joe in the bathroom to shave. So one morning it made a wrong turn in the hallway Uncle Joe and broke up the family."

"And from this humble beginnings you grew up to be the darling from Society. Loved, adored. . . . . Tel me, little one, why is it, the most alluring, the most bewitching, the most enchanting little girls . . . . the ones by whom is eyes like violet pools from mystery. Why do they always think the worst about their husbands? Fenimore adores you, child! Often in his sleep . . . . oh yes, he takes sometimes in the afternoon on his desk a semester . . . . often in his sleep I hear him talk from you. Like this:

" 'Let me take you in my arms my loved one. Let me I should crush you close . . . . like this! Let me drink in kisses filled with dreams . . . . like this! Let me hug you. Let me toss you on a. . . . .' Yi yi yi yi yi! . . . . But what do I'm doing? Forgive me my child I . . . . I. . . . You got maybe a whisk-broom? Heh Heh! Thanks. So you see, babe, put it out from you mind that it goes around married men on the make. It just happened that it went your Fenimore berserk a trifle. So is what. He didn't ate a eclair. Sometimes it could causing gallstones eclairs. Places he'll go far irregardless. Plans I got for him tremendous. And with him, by his side, a splendid woman, one with looks, with brains! . . . . like you! Places you will go far too! So take by me some fatherly advice, my child. Forgive him when he comes back home. Take my tip, babe. Make for him a joyous welcome. Forgive the jer . . . . forgive him! Here is from the firm a petty cash advance from fifty dollars. Go shopping in the Market. Go prepare for the return from the prodigal, a meal a sumptious one. Home to the fireside welcome him. With forgiveness envelop him. And so soon what he arrives . . . . this is the main thing . . . .

75

"Heavens, child! What do I'm doing?"

so soon what he arrives, you'll let me know . . . . Is from here a back way out?"

Departures it took Mister Fizwell. Gaily it trilled Missus Figgits a song. In the eyes was by her a sparkle. In the voice, laughter. To shopping in the market she started out. . . . .

In the washroom it was concluding to the gentleman on the floor Mister Figgits his narrigation, so:

"So you see, I didn't ate a eclair, and now give gradually a look!"

Up it gave the gentleman from the floor a leap . . . . The hand from Mister Figgits he begins to shake like it should be an auto jack . . . . Heartily he is giving him slaps on the back . . . . Speeches he is making to him so:

"Let me be the first to do you honor. sir! It's off to you my hat!"

"You sure," inquired Mister Figgits, anxiously, "that from the sock by the jaw you not cuckoo?"

"Look a modest hero!" gave excamations the gentleman. "Monuments to a man like you they should erecting. On every street corner yet . . . . instead from lampposts! A privilege it is to shake a man like you the hand! Honored I am, sir. Fergisham is my name . . . . but to you—Fergy!"

Speechless with agape stood Mister Figgits.

"You mean," he managed to ejaculate, "that you grasping . . . . you understanding, why it was by me a unwillingness to eat a eclair?"

"Look a humility on the part from a great man!" made responses Fergy. "One against the world he stands. Bloody with unbowed by him the head! One against the world! And let me assure you pal, that the world is by you already conquered. On account it's conquered inside from you the lusts with the desires, with the appetites from a carnival nature! Congratulations let me heap on you! On the fingers from Three-fingered Gooch could be counted heroes like you. Robert Fulton! Pasteur! Curie! Woodrow Wilson! . . . . You!"

"You mean," gave gasps from unbelief Mister Figgits, "that . . . ."

"A shrine will be erected here!" made interruptions, Fergy. "Pilgrimages will make unto it pilgrims! It awaits the world a man like you my friend. A profit to unlock the doors from wisdom. To shed forth the light from knowledge. Moses they found in the bullrushes! You they found here!"

"We sure find ourselves sometimes in strange places," made modest observations Mister Figgits. What in this moment it gave a ring the coin-box phone on the wall.

Statements now made Fergy:

"This would be for me, I got suspicions. Hello!"

The remainder from the conversation came out from Fergy in a low voice. Also from one side from the mouth, it came out. All that it was able Mister Figgits unavoidably to decipher was that

"Monuments they'll make to you!"

on the other end from the wire was a party entitled Sugar. Also that Sugar was at the moment impatiently waiting on a street corner for Fergy to keep with her a appointment. Soothingly made Fergy promises to Sugar, that in five minutes he'll be sure to meet her. And to Mister Figgits then he turns for farewells:

"Sadly my friend we come now to the parting from the ways. A deed from charity I go now out to do!"

"Charity?" gave echoes Mister Figgits, "This is a very notable procedure."

"Ah yes!" gave musings Fergy, "This little protege from mine . . . . this Sugar. Sweet home girl . . . . the sensible type! None from the flibberty-gibberty bobby-sox variety. So is by her a brother. Poor boy. Yes . . . . up here in the head. Used to was a boogie-woogie player. Couldn't do nothing for him now the greatest doctors. Till last week. Fortunately I was able to do at this time for a imminent specialist . . . . the greatest in the country . . . . a big favor. A pound butter I got for him. So to me he says, 'Fergy, boy . . . . any time, any place! Just name it!' I told him I would like to escorting to him Sugar in the office. She should have with him a constellation regarding from her brother. 'Done!' exclaims the great man . . . . And now Figgits my friend . . . . my fine with noble friend, I'm on my way to . . . . ouch . . . . Oh! . . . . Oh! . . . ."

"Yi yi!" gave anxious queries Mister Figgits, "You not well gradually?"

"Is nothing . . . . nothing . . . . Just my head . . . . I felt all from a sudden faint with dizzy . . . . I . . . . with a blinding flash!"

"From where through the booth I gave you innocently the punch . . . . Oh my!"

"I'll be all ri . . . . oh, what could was all those black spots by me in front from the eyes? . . . . It swims by me the room. Whistles I hear blowing. Horns with whistles. But go I must. Help me

Galahad, help me on my horse. . . . ."

"Galahad! Horse! Yi yi yi! It sees the poor chap dilutions! Oh what did I did, with my impestuous blow! Here friend. You not eligible to travel. Let me I should taking Sugar for you to the doctor. . . . ."

"Hark it blows the trumpets angels . . . . what's that? You said you'll take her to the doctor . . . . Well I didn't wished to suggesting it pal, but now that you bringing it up, I . . . . I. . . . . Black is spinning clouds in front from me. Dark it grows the night . . . . Carry on friend Figgits . . . . Lay me down here . . . . Go . . . . Carry on . . . . To you from falling hands the torch I . . . . Go . . . . Doctor . . . . Sugar . . . . Corner. Front from Shooting Gallery . . . . Go . . . . go. . . . ."

Out from the door it flew Mister Figgits. And so soon what he was out, it gave nimbly up from the floor a leap Fergy, and out through the skylight gave in the opposite direction a vanish. What in this moment it came in the Grand Mufti from the washroom with a white coat with a whisk broom and speeches made disgustedly:

"Give a look all sorts from crums they letting in here since the war. A trade in here a classy one we used to had, but now is only in the dough the stinkers! Pfooey."

"Pasteur! Curie! Woodrow Wilson!" kept soliloquizing Mister Figgits to himself! What in this moment he arrived by the corner in the front from the Shooting Gallery. Standing there was only one person which belonged in the category from females. Up and down the sidewalk she is, pacing . . . . tapping on the flagstones with a toe. On the lips with lipstick she is painting. Also blowing from a butt a puff. For two blocks in each direction from her is smelling the atmosphere gradually like a perfume vending machine. All over the nylons is by her chalk marks from a traffic cop for overparking.

80

Impatiently was waiting Sugar.

Venturesomely gives approaches Mister Figgits:
"Sugar?"

"Ankle off, flatfoot!"

"Poor little creature," gave responses Mister Figgits, "I could see on account from you poor brother, you are all agrog with consternation. So be from good cheer. From Fergy I'm a emmisary. He suffers from a indisposal which is making him ineligible to travel. So in lieu from him, my child, allow me I should escort you to the Doctor."

"So, cut out the bloop, and start escorting," made replies the maiden, while in the same time is pulling up to a halt in front from them a taxicab without a license. And for twenty-two miles via the taxicab it consisted the conversation a remark from Mister Figgits:

"Is worried something terrible Fergy over you brother!" To

81

With chalk marks on the nylons yet, for over parking.

which made replies Sugar:

"You don't kidding, jerk!"

For the rest from the way is again Mister Figgits saying to himself, "Pasteur . . . . One against the world . . . . Me with Woodrow Wilson. Monuments yet."

What gradually they attain in the front from the Doctor's house an arrival.

Grim with eerie is the house from a old frame nature yet. With steps a flight from steep ones attached to the front. Up the steps it makes ascensions Mister Figgits holding gallantly Sugar by the arm. By the door on the buzzer he gives a buzz. Open creaks the door, and is standing in front from them a individual accoutered in a costume from a butler. What to him makes remarks Sugar:

"Hello Dracula."

Tactfully is smiling Mister Figgits to the butler and in a modu-

The rest from the way, Mister Figgits talks to himself—
Monuments! . . . ."

lated voice from dignity is saying:

"We should like please we should see the Doctor!" Beckonings
it makes them the butler down a hall, a long one, dark with
gloomy. Open he throws from an alcove the drapes. Lights from
two candles is there glaring. Under the candles, in a horizontal
position is a black shiny casket! And occupying it, a gentleman
a distinguished one with a Van Dyke beard yet. What respect-
fully gives a whisper the butler.

"Here he is . . . . Sudden, didn't it was? Last night. Some fish
he ate!"

Gasps with splutters gave Mister Figgits. "You mean he
croaked?"

What replies made the butler, "I assure you sir, we not rehearsing!"

And in the same time is emitting Sugar a scream from a blood-

83

Grim with eerie was the Doctor's house!

curdling nature, and on the floor she is giving a swoon.

Crowding now around it people with advice. The doctor's niece is Sugar now mistaken for. Suggesting is someone for her glass from water. Insisting is another one, the open air. And in

To the funeral went Mister Figgits.

the same time is giving the butler to Mister Figgits taps on the shoulder with announcements:

"We about ready to start now, sir. You, with the young woman will riding in car four. I'm sure it'll cause the fresh air by her a revival."

Expostulations begins to splutter Mister Figgits. Surrounded he is by pushing crowds. Vainly he makes protests. Bundled he gets with the unconscious Sugar into a car. Dazed he is, with too bewilted to remonstrate! Off it gives a start the funeral procession. While in the same time gaily is shopping in the market, with a shopping bag, Missus Figgits. She should preparing sumptuously a dinner to welcome with forgiveness home, the Prodigal Mister Figgits. . . . .

Mopping with a handkerchief the brow in the car for five blocks is Mister Figgits. Slightly he is now reconciled to the trip on the grounds what to himself he is reminding.

"Fourteen dollars cab fare, cost me to come here! So why I should refuse a lift?"

What in this moment it gives a revival Sugar with questions, dazed ones:

"Where do I am?"

Enlightenments makes Mister Figgits. Rented becomes the air with screams, with shrieks, with yells, hysterical ones. Like a wildcat is fighting Sugar and howling let me out from here, it's hard luck.

Dives she makes through the window. Shattered is the glass. A wild grab in the niche from time makes Mister Figgits. Apart in his hands comes Sugar's dress. On the sidewalk flies off from

Slightly he is reconciled to the trip.

the populace the hats, while by one leg Mister Figgits is hauling Sugar back into the car. Smeared he gets with powder rouge, with lipstick. Reminders he attempts to give from the sacredness from the occasion . . . . one not for tears but rather beauty . . . . the great adventure . . . . the weary pilgrim on the homeward trail . . . . the solemn seraphic journey to that bourne from which no traveller. . . . ."

"Leggo me leg, before I kick your teeth in!" gives yells with struggles Sugar. . . . .

Via judo methods tries now Mister Figgits he should calm her. Grips he gets in terribly embarrassing places. A knee he gets in the eye, making immediately the optic blue. Frantic to the driver he is making now appeals. With shrugs responds the driver, expressions in his face denoting:

"Don't go pawing the dames, pal, and jams like this you'll won't get into!"

Piggy-back is now bouncing Mister Figgits, with Sugar all over the car. Tattoos is beating on his head the roof. With one hand over her nose with mouth he is stifling by her the squeals. Black is Sugar getting in the face. And by William Cullen Bryant, he recites, to calm her, Thanitopsis:

> "So live, that when thy summons comes to join
> The innumerable caravan that moves . . . . ouch! . . . .
> To the pale realms of shade . . . . stop scratching!
> Where each shall take his chamber in the silent
> halls from . . . . Oww!!"

A wrench a frantic one gives Sugar. Like a crocodile it snaps her jaws on three from Mister Figgits' fingers. Through the glass he goes head first into the driver. Up the curbstone sails the car. Fainting on the sidewalk is pedestrians. Over a baby's face it throws a mother quick a shopping bag. On a stepladder it had started in respect a lamp-light cleaner he should doff his hat, but he fell from shock head first instead into his bucket water.

On the sidewalks crowds is gasping!

By both ankles now is grabbing Mister Figgits onto Sugar like a wheelbarrow. Around in circles they are hopping. A heel gets Mister Figgits in the nose. Half way out the door is hanging Sugar, garbled only in a slip with step-ins. . . . .

Desperate is Mister Figgits. Memories he suddenly gets that when he was a little boy, so whenever he would undergo a tantrum it would sing to him his mother, "The Owl With The Pussycat!" And soothingly would give a vanish by him the tantrum. So, desperately, with one knee on her chest, Mister Figgits commences to sing to Sugar, "The Owl With The Pussycat," so:

> *"Oh the Owl with the Pussycat went to sea*
> *In a beautiful boat, a pea green one.*
> *They took along honey, with plenty from money,*
> *With a Sinatra album, a mean one!"*

Desperate is Mister Figgits.

Fruit it bears immediately the idea. By Sugar gives instantly a evaporation the hysteria. Serene with untruffled she becomes. Relaxative she sits back. The legs she crosses. A Camel she lights. Continuations from the Owl with the Pussycat makes Mister Figgits.

"Oh lovely Sugar, Sugar my love
What a beautiful Sugar you are."

What in this moment, red turns a traffic light. Directly in front from a Public Market halts the procession. On the sidewalk in front from the Market, in her arms a shopping bag, a full one, is standing Missus Figgits! While gaily, with a imaginary guitar yet in the hands, is singing in the car to Sugar, Mister Figgits:

"What a beautiful Sugar you are . . . . you are,
What a beautiful Sugar you are.

The Astrologer told me to expect today a revelation.

So let us be married,
Too long we have tarried,
And we'll dance by the light from the Moon .... the Moon.
And we'll dance by the light ...... Yi Yi!

"My wife! Phoebe! Darling, I could explain everything ....
don't give by conclusions a jump!"

"First," made responses Missus Figgits, "We'll give in the
car a jump!" What in this moment green turned the light,
greener turned Mister Figgits, another Camel it lit Sugar, and
proceeding is the procession. . . . .

"God is good!" makes intonations Missus Figgits, "It told me
the astrologer I should expect to-day a revelation!"

"Have respect for the dead!" made cautions Mister Figgits.

"You not dead yet .... but you getting awful warm. . . . ."

"Now, honey. . . . ."

"I heard from everything . . . . And you too, my half-nude bleach job, I'm quite sure! I heard from Auto Courts! I heard from Boat Houses! I heard even from Telephone Booths . . . . But a funeral. . . . . Well . . . . well we living and we learning is no letch? . . . . Ha? All over town is searching for you Mister Fizwell to close up that parcel real estate in Laurelton, and by funerals you gallivanting on Main Street. I thought I heard from everything. But a funeral! . . . . From a party yet I never met even socially! A professional mourner you became maybe on the side, dog? A couple bucks to chisel maybe, ha? Or maybe the invitation you hid from me, ha . . . . Maybe social, you ashamed to being seen with me already by functions, ha heel? So with glamorous companions you. . . . ."

"Darling . . . . please . . . . I . . . . I had to take the young lady to a doctor. He's up front, you could ask . . . . No on second thoughts you. . . . ."

"To a doctor! You got to take a young lady! Saints preserve us! Brazenly you flaunt me this . . . . Oh you beast . . . . you callous creature . . . . you vile contemptible wretch. At last is off the mask. From behind the tree you're out! How long it's going on behind my back all this . . . .?

"One hour. . . . ."

"One hour? . . . . he's drunk yet besides!"

"Darling . . . . my dear . . . . Things I admit look slightly bad. . . . ."

"Slightly he says yet!" gave screams Missus Figgits. "Slightly bad!" You see, dearie, what I up against with this worm!"

"You mean Wayward Hayward, here?" gave a nod Sugar.

"Oh the wretch!" wailed Phoebe, "Oh the callous wastrel. Red-handled I catch him canoodling, with a trollop like you yet, and stubbornly, brazenly he denies. . . . ."

"But darling, I am guiltless! . . . . Do you hear me — guiltless!"

"Low contemptible worm! Why couldn't you once admit something . . . . Admit once!"

"But Darling, how could I make from guilt admittances, when innocent I am?"

"You see, dearie! Twenty years this goes on. Did it ever once admit the worm something? Oh no! Did he ever left burning a light in the bathroom? Not him! Oh you profligate . . . . you scamp! Who broke in the parlor my Mink vase? . . . . Don't look at him! From the ice-box was he ever the one what ate the cold leg lamb? Perish the thought! . . . . Twenty years. Oh you sinful brute! I getting so riled up! I getting so boiling! I getting so frustrated! For my nerves this is no good! My dizzy spells. I'll getting back again. Spots I'll start to see again in the front from the eyes . . . . So please . . . . I beg from you Fenimore . . . . if you've got left a spark from infection for me . . . . Confess! Own up once like a man. Get it off from you mind. . . . . I'll feel much better!"

Frantic is poor Mister Figgits. Desperately at the bottom he is loving his wife. Straws he clutches at.

"Here, driver! You a innocent banister. This is my wife. Explain her . . . . please!"

Grunts gave the driver:

"Look, pal. Six o'clock I got up this morning. Sunburn I got a bad case from. With a hang-nail with a bit tongue yet! Burnt for breakfast was the toast. Busted is the washing machine! By my wife fell out a inlay. Living with us is in-laws. From in-laws with inlays I'm going nuts. So please . . . . dont make me more trouble!"

"Darling!" shouted Mister Figgits, "You got to believe me!"

"Confess! Confess, once like a man . . . . not a weasel. Confess . . . . horrible as it is I'll shut my eyes . . . . I'll blot out . . . . I'll . . . . even forgive you! But just confess! Please confess!"

"I should confess in order you should forgive? To believe me you refuse, but for confessions you'll forgive?"

"Oh you beast! You stubborn beast. Pipes with slippers I was getting ready. Waiting was the love seat. Hams with turkeys I ran out to buy. Look! Hams with turkeys. What I'll do with them now? Boo-hoo-oo! What'll I do with the hams with turkeys?"

"Dump 'em in the kitty with the wreaths with flowers, sister," made suggestions Sugar. "Tell 'em it's from Dr. Fu Manchu a tribute . . . . a fellow colleague . . . . Or better still that it's you grandfather part Mandarin!"

"One more crack from you!" snarled Phoebe, "and you'll be part bow-legged from a paste in the mush!"

"Oh yeah?"

"Yeah! Go on . . . . start something! You'll be so laid up, darling, that for a month you won't be back in bed! And as for you, vile wretch, my ultimato you now got! Home I am going . . . . sniff sniff . . . . There I will waiting. With a box orchids you'll returning. Penitent you'll confessing. And to my chased bosom, I'll clasping you forgivingly! Out I'll get by the corner . . . . Waiting I'll be in the love seat. Farewell it's now or au revoir!"

Open it gave Phoebe a fling the door. Out from the car a step she made bravely, with the nose high in the air. Splashes a minute later echoed all over the avenue. And from far down below, unladylike came remarks:

"!!*##"***Manholes!"

"Should I go home, should I not go home."

SITTING on a Park bench is Mister Figgits. Flower boxes full from orchids is by him in the lap.

Indecisions for hours he is making. One minute, to go home he commences, and so soon what up he gets, then down again he sits! Making to himself interrogations so:

Confessions it insists my wife I should make. Which in this case, my sins she'll forgive. Till here is good. But now I ask myself, how could it be a person forgiven for a thing which in the first place he didn't did? Hm. . . . . Already I'm getting slightly from all this a headache. Maybe is better I should withdraw the question, go home, cop a plea, take a rap. Ready will then be for me again the pipe with the slippers, with dinner on time. A respectable man once more I am. And to the neighbor's dog I'll say again good morning.

In which case I am asking, is this being with myself honest? So to this I give an answer. Who is today with himself, honest? For example Figgits, did it really whispered to you a voice in the Cafe, you shouldn't eat the eclair? Did it whispered to you a voice on the road, you shouldn't step on the bettle? Was it ever in the first place there a beetle on the road at all? Or a road? Careful now! Hm. . . . . You do not wish to answer, ha! So let us to rephrase the question. Do you gamble by the Stock Market?

No!

Why you don't gamble by the Stock Market?

I don't believe in speculations.

So what do you doing with you money?

I putting it in the Bank.

And what does the Bank doing with it?

It's investing it in stocks with bonds.

You see, Figgits? To be really honest with yourself, you got to go and live in a cave. With your asthma yet! Go home, be happy!

You mean dishonestly I should confessing to a guilt from which I'm innocent in order to be happy? In this case I would all my life living in a Fool's Parasite!

So who isn't living these days in a Fool's Parasite? But if it's aware the Fool that it's by him a Fool's Parasite, then it's no longer a Parasite. Which is defeating the whole purpose. Like it should lie a lady about her age to the Astrologer . . . . Hm. Could I using at this point a aspirin!

So wait . . . . Let's from another angle we should tackling it.

95

Confucius is telling us that if it wishes a man to rule a empire, so first must be by him peace with harmony among the family. In order it should be by a man in the family, peace with harmony, so first is got to be by him self-discipline .... Aha .... Keep going Fenimore, I think you got now something .... Not to eat a eclair is tantamount to self-discipline. Is no? Now we getting places. Because from self-discipline you achieve in the family harmony.

Harmony comes from discipline. Discipline comes from not eating a eclair. You didn't eat a eclair——yi. So, look a harmony! A shambles, a Cafe. A cop with a broken jaw! Wrecked, a public washroom! Loused up by a Doctor a funeral. By my wife caught red-handled in a comprising canoodle with a blonde! .... Some harmony! Maybe I should read a little more Confucius. Or maybe better still a little less. Hm! let's we should starting again.

My father, what he was a man, in the same place for fifty-seven years in business, so always he said so:

"A wife is a contradicture. A man is a dope. Married he gets in a moment from mental apparition. Home it then runs him the wife, like from a bargain basement with a prize package. And the strings she can't rip off fast enough she should begin to examine it for flaws."

True! The smartness from my not eating a eclair it refuses my wife to take notice from. Only the dumbness! My trouble is that I'm smart. If I was a moron, happily would I be unaware from all this. And home I would now be concocting a highball. But then I would be dumb. On the other hand—who is smarter? A moron what thinks he's a genius? Or a genius what knows he's a moron? Maybe is better I should be smart like a moron, I should go home and confess.

In this case, she'll make me promise I should never do it again. But how could I not do something again, that in the first place I never did at all. And if I didn't did it, why should I confess?

If I confess, then I'm not honest. If I'm honest, I got to live in a tree. If I live in a tree, I'm a moron. If I'm a moron, I'm brilliant. If I was brilliant, I'd go home. For what?

For a wifely coddle, a pretty frock, a kiss with a caress, and she should tell me if my sox is on the right side. For this, I should give up maybe a chance to occupy in posterity a niche? To become immortal from not eating a eclair is now by me a great opportunity. Pasteur! Curie! Woodrow Wilson! Hmm. Figgits my boy, you are now by a cross-forks in the road. Like is saying William Shakespeare:

> *There is a tide in the affairs from men*
> *Which taken during a flood, leads on to Fortune*
> *Omit it. Hm! So all the voyage from you life*
> *Is bound in shallows in conjunction yet*
> *With Misery*
> *And if I take him now,*
> *How many times shall this my lofty scene,*
> *In which I did not eat a chocolate eclair,*
> *Be acted out again, in states unborn*
> *And accents yet unknown!*

Hm! A sharp Joe, this Shakespeare. A psychology course he could clean up with to-day. My lofty scene! States unborn! . . . . In countless future states will thousands watch me yet not eat an eclair in effigy! In future High Schools yet . . . . each year a Pageant. Me not eating a eclair! So go act out someone not eating a eclair! How will it look? First will be with a chorus trumpets, a solo. Then by the Dean a address. And then it wouldn't eat someone a eclair. Hm! Frankly it stinks. Besides it's getting chilly here on the bench. Drizzles is commencing. Sizzling on the stove is home now pot roast with potato pancakes. Up from the love seat will give my Phoebe a jump to forgive me. A home with a fireside with peace with contentment will I having. To Di Maggio let them put up monuments! Home I'm heading for!"

In front from Mister Figgits stood a tramp!

Up from the bench gave a jump Mister Figgits. Standing in front from him was a tramp. Woebegone! Down with out! Miserable, bedraggled!

Gasps from horror with pity gave Mister Figgits.

"My poor fellow! Tell me, how did it ever befelt to you such a misfortune?"

Out he whipped a banjo!

"It's worth a buck to you to hear it, Mac?"

"Of course, my poor fellow. Here!"

Out whipped the derelict a banjo. A homemade one from a cigar box. Sagas he began to chant from a Calypso nature, combined a trifle with the Ancient Mariner, and rendered in the manner from a Strolling Troubador:

> "*Oh listen to me people,*
> *Listen to my tale a sad one.*
> *A home with a happy family,*
> *Long years ago I had one.*

A Pet Shop also did I owned,

With a wife with seven brats.

And in the Shop a blondie . . . wow!
To feed the dogs with cats . . .

Oh, her cheeks like lillies pure, were white,
It shone her eyes like gems,
By her was lips like rosebuds, yi!
And what a pair from stems!

It was torrid, sultry, slinking,
Every move what made this cutie,
What gave wolf calls all day long the pets
With whistles, "Sweet Patootie!"
Well a man is only human,
Long it didn't was,
Till where Papa had no business,
He was mixing in the schnozze!
Oh brother take from me a tip,
Put on your hat with coat,
What yens you get for blondies,
Grab the first banana boat!

Suspicious grew my Missus,
On account she had a sister

What for twenty-seven years or more
A man it didn't kissed her.
Schemes cooked up the sister,
She planned them all alone,
How me the wife should trapping
With a homemade dictaphone.
In the back room from the Pet Shop
On a cage she hung a towel.

Inside the cage a parrot sat,
And outside sat a owl.
Outside made observations
From the goings on, the owl,
And waylayed them to the parrot
Who was hiding in the towel.

With witnesses the Missus then,
The parrot cage unveiled.
It spilled the dirt the parrot
My heart it almost failed!

Then advice it gave the sister
To my wife, "My dear, of course,
For alimony lots you'll sue
The bum with a divorce!"
The Courtroom full was crowded,
The Judge sat on the Bench yet,
Reporters it was jammed with
Spanish, Greek with French yet!
Each the juicy details
They should spread from my fiasco,
Which scandalous was hotter
Than a bucket from Tabasco!
Then suddenly it came a hush,
You could hear a pin drop, Mister,
When up in Court it jumped my wife
And double-crossed her sister!
A speech she made a noble one,
With cheers came down the house.
It rang the rafters to her words,
"I forgive my erring spouse!

So it sues a wife a husband,
So she wins, so then she'll lose him.
Better he should start anew
By the wife's forgiving bosom!"
Oh brother take from me a tip,
You shouldn't get caught nappin',
From a wife to be forgiven,
To a dog it shouldn't happen!
She forgave me in the morning,
She forgave me in the night!

If a bottle beer I opened,
If my pipe I tried to light,
Snatched away was each one,
With a kick yet in the shins,
While speeches made the Missus
Forgiving me my sins!
Oh, better with a fire axe
She bashed me in my head,

Or with a blunderbuss she pumped
My system full from lead.
Oh, brother, if you ask me
To you I'll give an answer
By a wife to be forgiven
Sooner you should wish a cancer.
I used to had a bankroll,
My small-change now she steals.
She reads my correspondence,
She hounds me during meals.
Orders from me she once took,
In my name was all accounts,
If chops for lunch I ordered,
To the chop-house she would bounce.
Lord with Master was I once,
My power as autonomous.
Each move that made the wife with kids
Was with my will synonomous!
My pipe I used to smoke in bed,
Regardless what it smelt like.

The Sunday funnies I read first,
I got up when I felt like!

Stamps for my collection
My kids they used to save me,
But this was all in the good old days,
Before my wife forgave me!
For hours I could ramble on,
But what's the use . . . . you ketch!
A diagram you'll wouldn't need
From the downfall from a wretch.
So brother, if you see a wretch,
What's all devoid from mirth,
A beaten mutt, a sad one,
A walking Hell on earth,

Who creeps in corners, dark ones,
Who slinks by hidden nooks,

Who on his face exclusively
Wears miserable looks,
Who the best professors couldn't do
A thing for . . . . it should save him,
You looking brother on a man
What once his wife forgave him!

Out from the love seat gave a jump Missus Figgits. Ringing was the doorbell. Open a fling, forgivingly she gave the door. Standing there was a messenger. In the hand was by him a flower box, it should be inside orchids. Open it gave a rip Missus Figgits the box. So instead from orchids, was inside a rope. In the rope was a loop. In the loop was a knot. What altogether it consisted the whole thing from a noose.

5

Iɴ ʜᴇʀ ʟɪᴛᴛʟᴇ room, which consisted in the Fizwell domain, from the maid's quarters, was sitting in her rocker Ingrid.

On the walls from floor till ceiling was pasted all over pictures from Mister Fizwell . . . . pin-up ones. From the ceiling hung a bunch bananas . . . . for days untasted. Deep sighs, wistful ones with lovelorn, was making Ingrid by each picture. While from the rear section from a pulp magazine she was reading advertisements so:

LOVE PILLS

Pasha's Potent Potion!

Two pills in a cup coffee, girls . . . . HE'S YOURS!
MONEY BACK IF NOT SATISFIED
SEND 26 cents in stamps

PASHA PRODUCTS . . . . DEP'T G, Arsenic, N.Y.

Also Mfrs. of Pasha's Wrinkle Remover.
Ventriloquist Course. 60 Sensational
Song Poems. False Teeth Fastener. And
Six Decks from Fortune Telling Cards.

114

In her rocker in her room sat Ingrid.

With a scissors it gave Ingrid swiftly a cut out from the page the advertisement. Thirteen two-cent stamps she folded in it, and the whole thing she put in an envelope. In this moment came a knock by her on the door.

Quickly, under her apron it put Ingrid, in hiding, the envelope and commenced hastily to knit a snood. While with a false gaiety she gave invitations:

"Come in gradually!"

Into the room gave a waft Begonia.

"On the snoop eh?" gave greetings Ingrid.

"Did it was Fizwell able to extract from Missus Figgits, the paper, dearie?"

"Did you was able to extract from Sinatra a date?"

"Still in the grease eh!" gave comments Begonia.

"You don't know the half from it, dearie. Poor Mister Fizwell . . . . He gets from all sides. Privately dearie, it's no help to him that wife from his. Of course, I only a ape, but privately is no help to any one a wife. Still less a help to any one is Philpot!"

"The stupe with the aluminum yarmulka? He's the one what put the whole deal on a crutch. Is no?"

"And how he put it! Instead from affecting between Mister with Missus Figgits, a reconsolidation, he fixed it so she kicked him out in the street. Solace then sought Mister Figgits with a flooze, a blonde one. A doctor, I think they both murdered. He disappeared. Privately, I think he ran with the huzzy away to the South Seas. On a island he strumps now a banjo, and the creature dances a whole time in front from him. I had a brother who took from Borneo once a two weeks cruise. He told me how they living there . . . . dun't esk!"

"Privately," gave sighs Begonia, "It don't sound bad! I had a Uncle once who ran away with a Midget to Patagonia. Like larks they were happy. Elevator shoes it wore the Midget. Except epsom-minded sometimes she would put on one elevator shoe with one plain shoe. So with hippity-hops she walked. What it kept bump-

A banjo he strumps and she dances in front from him.

ing him, her head in the jaw, and gradually punch-drunk he became. So where is now Mister Fizwell? In the library? Hanging himself maybe?"

"Would I be sitting here sending away for Pasha's . . . . oops! . . . . Would I be knitting here a snood if it was hanging himself poor Mister Fizwell. The three from them are now desperately by Missus Figgits in the house. Outside of course in the car is waiting Philpot. In order it shouldn't recognize him Missus Figgits with the dishpan over his head!"

6

OUTSIDE IN the front from the Figgits domicile sat Philpot waiting in the car. Inside was pleading something terrible, Fizwell with Wizwell to Missus Figgits, that she should still forgiving Fenimore. Adamant was Phoebe. Jelly beans she nibbled, in a rage, and gave screams:

"Nooses he sends me yet! . . . . Nooses! Insults on the top from injuries! My hands for five minutes I should get on him, the weasel. A noose I'd put his head into! Better he gives the place here a wide birth! And you too, gentlemen, if you'll excuse me very much!"

"My dear child . . . ." began Mister Fizwell.

"This is by me, with you already the second childhood, Mister Fizwell. . . . . Sorry!"

"But. . . . ."

"Confess, I begged him!" screamed unheeding Missus Figgits. . . . . "Just confess, that's all I ask! . . . . Like you told me Mister Fizwell. Confess, and I'll forgive you. I got witnesses. The flooze herself, the driver, and a gentleman in overalls who was protruding from a manhole at the time . . . . Confess, I begged him. Confessions did he make? Nooses he sent. . . . ."

"It's just the same with my wife," gave agreements Wizwell. "Cockeyed stinko I could coming home, and this, broad-mindedly

118

she tolerates. But, in the morning, if I don't have a hangover, it should split me up the head in pieces . . . . yi yi yi . . . . does she see red! Women they all. . . . ."

"Dummy up, dope!" gave a snarl Mister Fizwell, without moving his lips, a trick he learned from a friend, a former resident from San Quentin. At the same time he is turning to the Missus Figgits.

"A noose he sent you my dear? And this is causing by you truffled feelings in the little breast? Look, a child misconstructs from things the meanings. Did you ever heard from the language from the flowers?"

"Flowers? What's with flowers nooses got to do?"

"Hm, I knew you didn't knew. So let me, I'll explain. A girl, when she is wearing in the hair daisies, so this is in code a message meaning, 'Okay for Tuesday night!' If lilacs she is wearing, this is meaning, 'Lay off. I now engaged!' A boy is sending to the girl friend tulips, so this is denoting, 'Chow main, Friday?' And if it puts in the window box the girl friend pansies with a astor, this is meaning, 'Right!'

"But . . . . to tieing in a string a love-knot, and to sending to you wife the string inside a flower box. Yi Yi! Such a love, a hot one couldn't dream up even a Lord Bryan or a Judy Cassanova. You a very fortunate young woman!"

"You mean," gave hesitations Phoebe, "you mean it could was possible he didn't meant what I should hang myself?"

"My dear dear child. How could it ever insert itself into you pretty head, such a dignosis?"

"Flowers from languages maybe he's sending," gave responses Phoebe, "but seeds from doubt is still by me planted. Time I will need to arrive by a disbelief. Besides is now gradually four-thirty. And each afternoon, in this time I listen on the radio, to my favorite program, 'The Crazy Lady.' You'll find in the patio a bowl polly seeds, with two yo-yo sets, gentlemen."

A turn gave gradually on the dial Phoebe. But instead from

The Crazy Lady it came out from the radio, soothingly music, with a voice a suave one soft with rich:

"Instead from The Crazy Lady, which is going off the air on account it became the sponsor sane, so Station PQR takes great pleasure in bringing you the Hour from Peaceful Arbitration. From which we now ready to hear the next case. Number 86745-345 J. Do you consist from the gentleman involved, sir?"

So it gave a answer over the air a voice:

"I do!"

What up to the ceiling in astoundishment, gave a jump Fizwell, Wizwell with Phoebe with gasps yet:

"It's him . . . . It's Fenimore!"

"You may state you case," gave a purr the Announcer, "before this large with intelligent audience, in conjunction with our emi-

"Should a man be forced to confessing to a deed which he didn't did?"

nence Board from Peacemakers. Allow me first, however, I should introduce the Board. First is the Honorable P. P. Potwhistle III. Next is that military wizard with a tank, General Snackbarton Mudd. And in this corner our lady member—Miss Azela Fish-Wartberry, famous sociologist with tree chopping contest winner. State please you case, sir!"

"Is it fair," began Mister Figgits in a voice overpowdered with emulsion, "that a man should be forced to confess to a deed which he didn't did? Is it fair he should become a outcast with a Uriah . . . . shunted from Society . . . . a wanderer, a Ishmeal . . . . a target for leers with jeers with sneers . . . . I ask you! Three thousand years was also Tiberius unjustly accused . . . . And if to-day he was alive he would be perfectly innocent. . . . ."

"Get please to the point," made promptings the Announcer.

"I didn't ate a eclair . . . . but I love my wife!"

"You hear . . . . he loves you!" gave hisses Mister Fizwell to Phoebe in the ear. "He loves you girl. . . . . Quick! Outside is the car. Posthaste we'll flying to the Radio station. Over the air waves will be broadcast lovingly reunions! In front from all the people then I'll give to him a raise with a bonus . . . . And to-night by Ganzi in the Palm Room . . . . will we toss a shindig . . . . dun't esk! . . . . Quick . . . . into the car!"

By the wheel sat Philpot. In the middle sat Phoebe. And to Wizwell it turned Fizwell, and without moving the lips, gave whispers so:

"So soon we hit the Station, you'll grab dopey Figgits. Over the head you'll conk him and nail the paper. Then instead from the raise with the bonus with the shindig, we'll kick him down a flight from stairs. And together with him that shrew from a wife! I'm getting with her a little bit fed up. Sly, is no? Of course is sly! Who thought from it? Me? Who thinks from everything around here? Me! Step on it, senseless one by the wheel, and don't remove the dishpan. On account is by you a codicil on the driver's license, that with a dishpan over the head, you drive

121

Everything seems to be in order.

better than without one. We don't want now, trouble with a shamus!"

In the Broadcasting Studio sat a huge ensemblage people. By a table, with great wisdom, sat listening the Peacemakers. While was giving to his narrigation, Mister Figgits, a conclusion so:

"So you see . . . . I didn't ate a eclair . . . . There I was and here I am."

To the Honorable P. P. Potwhistle III, now turned the Arbitrator, with invitations so:

"Judge Potwhistle . . . . Your opinion from this exigency, we would deeply appreciating to hear!"

A clearing it gave the throat Judge Potwhistle. With a chuckle a depreciating one, from a slightly amused nature, he made utterances:

"Of course it's not this case without certain aspects, ludicrous ones! In fact if I may saying so, never in all my years by the bench with bar, did I was able to find a more idiotic, a more imbecilic, a more silly, inane excuse to start among people riots. Because it refused a fat dope, a foolish one, a moron, with a dim-wit, to eat in a Cafe a eclair! . . . . In my opinion the results are stupid, unnecessary, with totally avoidable!"

"With his learned Honor, I fully in concourse," interloped Miss

With the dishpan he drives better than without it.

Fish-Wartberry. "But first, however, we must not be prune to leap by a conclusion . . . . In this case we are doing exactly what it did his wife. Stupid we'll admit he is! A jerk from the first water . . . . this miserable wretch, standing here friendless, alone, sour, embittered, vengeful, ruined . . . . a failure! But let us we should ask ourselves a question. Behind all his stupidity . . . . what was by him in the mind . . . . In Switzerland. . . . ."

"With my two imminent colleagues I totally in rappaport," made chimings in the General, "Switzerland I don't know from.

But let us rather asking does it have a right a moron he should jump up in a Cafe....."

"Quiet, Brass!" came from the crowd a razz. "This is what our boys....."

"In Switzerland ...." began again Fish-Wartberry .... What butted in a voice:

"I speak for eighty-thousand pastry chefs!"

"Sit down bum!" came responses. What again began Miss Fish-Wartberry:

"In Switzerland....."

"My dear," it interloped the General, "we don't discussing here cheese. We discussing eclairs....."

To which was listening in all over the country the population so:

.... And comments they were making: ....

"This is seeming, my dear, most interesting a question. And not without a varied complecture from aspects quite profound. Is no?"

"Without a doubt, my love. Of course is obvious that in the first place the man was a fool. . . . ."

. . . . While up the street another couple gave on the problems opinions, cultured with intelligent ones. . . . .

"Oh . . . . You really thinking so. . . . ."

"Truly a subject from intrickking value. Especially from a point from view a sociological one, my pet!"

"Yet in it, my dearest, we see from a wife a obstuteness, with cupidity. . . . ."

"Indeedy . . . .!"

. . . . So up one street, down another, around the corner, hither with thither with yon, and out past the city limits was being continued the discussion with dignity and decorum yet.

"Just the kind from a subject from humane interest to promoting gradually a tropic from intelligent discussion, ha? Interesting a relationship between a wife with a eclair!"

"Yeah . . . . but who was the Doctor? This is what I wishing to be appraised of. . . . ."

"We must realizing on the outset . . . . that from one eclair the energy could send to the moon a rocket. . . . ."

"But my wife would never in the first place dare she should. . . . ."

"Oh, she wouldn't, ha. . . . . Well, let me tell you, in the first place about your wife a few things. . . . ."

What came in this moment pauses for station announcements so:

"You listening to the Committee from Peaceful Arbitration . . . . stay tuned please! We continuing peacefully with the arbitrations. What out from the Radio it came from the Honorable P. P. Potwhistle the voice so:

"Madam, if you'll mentioning to me once more Switzerland, I'll. . . . ."

"If I had here my hatchet," gave retorts Miss Fish-Wartberry. While up jumped again the individual proclaiming:

"I speak now for eighty-two thousand pastry chefs!" A sock by the jaw he got by way from a response. Busted over the head from P. P. Potwhistle was by the Missus Fish-Wartberry from the orchestra a fiddle. . . . . All over the balcony was slugging

each other factions from a pro-eclair, with a anti-eclair nature. And in front from the radios was following the program the population so:

"So maybe you'd like with blondies to take also a ride, rat?"
"Who's talking from blondies. I talking from eclairs."
"Ya fadder's eclair. . . . .!"
"Don't tell me!"
"! *** ??? . . . **** ! ! . . Yeah!"
"You and your soap operas!"
"You tail end of a *** ! ! . . . * * * !"
"It's a lie. I never snore."
"How about the time your old lady —"
"Don't change the subject."
"I'll change your face!"
"You and who else?"
"Just me and this meat axe."
"Yeah?"
"Yeah!"
"***!!!##?????*******!"

"All I know is. . . . ."

"You don't even know what day from the week this is."

"Don't I? Well, it's by us the silver wedding university. So there. . . . ."

"Congratulations! ! !"

"So, you telling me that if I wish to bite like this a eclair . . . .?"
"Shut up. I want the floor!"
"You got it."

"Take our American colleges. . . . ."
"How does colleges affect the price of fertilizer?"
"What's this got to do with his wife catching him?"
"Button up, jerk!"
"Ya fadder's button!"

"What's grand opera got to do with eclairs?"

"Ya fadder's grand opera!"

"From where do you think we get all our roaches in the kitchen? From you! ! !"

"Don't change the subject . . . . stick to eclairs."

"Maybe YOU'D like to confess something, ha rat?"

"I wish I would have something to confess. . . . ."

"But my dear Snodgrass, if not handled wisely, such a situation could causing damage!"

"In Switzerland my dear Wagstaff. . . . ."

"Stop yelling you brute. You want it should think the neighbors that you beat me? . . . ."

"So, now it comes out! You've been hating me all these years!"

"Who's talking like a horse's what?"

"By the words from the Prophet Allah....."
"Allah never had to eat a eclair."
"Pipe down, infidel."

"What puzzles me is last night we started with a simple four-round brawl. . . . ."

"Exactly Mortimer. If Figgits can start with one eclair a riot, why should we be satisfied with four rounds?"

"And what gets the public? A fish in the face!"

"Must we fight out here among a plague from seventeen-year Arabs?"

"Better out here, than inside in front from the children."

"Sacre! Sapristi! Cuchon! Sale Vache! Eclairs!"

"Who says you couldn't keeping in refrigerators eclairs?"
"Ya fadders eclair! What about inflation, bollweevils, taxes, jive, with nylons?"

"We must shorten, tighten, control, curtail, consolidate, unite, and combine."

"I disagree!"

"I warn you sir, this in an international incident."

"We couldn't find a better spot!"

"Boom!"

EXTRA . . . . WORLD COURT MEETS . . . DELE-
GATES FLY . . . . LEAVES CANCELLED . . . .
EMBASSIES BUZZ . . . . SIAM ORDERS NINE BRIEF
CASES . . . . WIRE TAPPERS CONSCRIPTED . . . .
HEATTER YELLS KEEP COOL . . . . ENVOYS
CUTTING RED TAPE . . . . SCOTCH CUTTING
SCOTCH TAPE . . . . BOOTLEGGERS CUTTING
SCOTCH . . . . . EXTRA, EXTRA, STOCKS HITTING
LOW . . . . REFEREE WARNS STOCKS . . . .
STOCKS RALLY . . . . NYLONS RUN . . . . BEANS
JUMP . . . . BUTTER FREEZES . . . . EGGS CRACKS
. . . . TRAFFIC JAMS . . . . NIAGARA FALLS . . . .
EXTRA, EXTRA, EXTRA, STOP . . . . KING AD-
DRESSES SIX THOUSAND DELEGATES . . . .
SAYS STOP . . . . QUEEN ADDRESSES SIX THOU-
SAND INVITATIONS TO PARTY . . . . KING SAYS
PLEASE STOP . . . . EXTRA MEETING CALLED
TO ORDER . . . . CHAIRMAN OPENS MEETING
WITH GAVEL . . . . DELEGATE OPENS CHAIR-
MAN WITH GAVEL . . . . THE MEETING IS ON
. . . . STOP!

140

"Ootchka, brootchka, gzznyazzka eclair!"
"Gromootchka Izvzzanya Gooka Figgits Polish Corridor!"
"Gazzvitska fadder's corridor!"
"Blondie, Sugar, Manchuko. . . . .!"
"Blootchka Switzerland Mene Mene Tekle Upharsin!"
"Up yours too!"
"Brazzatzka oil wells Mandates Pampas!"
"Ya grampa's pampas!"
"Smile when you say grampa's pampas!"
"Ha, ha, ha . . . . grampa's pampas!"
"Blookotchnik you!"
"I'm insulted."
"In here expect to be insulted."
BIFF! . . . . .

AND . . . .

GROMYKO .... WALKS .... OUT!!

All over creation it rushed to the mikes news broadcasters with the latest news.....

"Well, here they go again, folks . . . . And this time it looks like a wang-doodle! Yessiree they got the tomahawk dug up . . . . they hanging by a eyelash. . . . . Take a tip from you reporter folks . . . . hang onto all you pennies . . . . Gonna be some buys sensational ones, in real estate down there . . . . Won't be able anyone to tell their home town from a hole in the ground. Won't be anybody there to tell . . . . ha ha. That's two jokes folks! Hold it . . . . Just came in from our Meteoric Bureau a warning . . . . Citizens attention. If any minute gives a zip across the sky a orange streak, and in the sun a vanish . . . . Dont worry! I repeat—don't worry . . . . It's just the Earth . . . . doing in grand style a off to Buffalo. . . . . Still tuning up folks . . . . Sure a breed from cats a queer one . . . . One half from them sweating nights that human life a hundred years should be prolonged. The half knocking itself out concocting rays to wipe out in five seconds the human race . . . . And for years they trying they should get in touch with us yet! Heh! Any time we wanted all we had to do was press a button! So who wants to buddy up with crackpots . . . . Who wants to getting folksy with a rich but looney cousin? Not this reporter, kids! Hold it . . . . just a minute folks . . . . looks like there is still a chance

uh . . . . uh . . . . Not so good. Look who's giving out a crawl

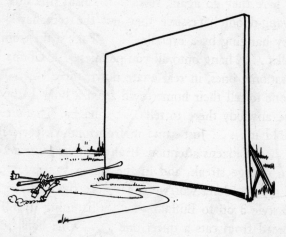

. . . . Curtains boys . . . . It's sure too bad . . . . Well, Winchell tried his best to stop them . . . . but . . . . Just a second, folks. . . . . Something going on down there . . . . lots from excitement over in one corner . . . . can't make out yet what they are saying . . . . They waiting for a bulletin . . . . a important one . . . . and . . . . just a second folks . . . . here it's coming. . . . .

"AND HERE IT IS! ! ! !"

"Yippee!"

"Proclamations makes Gromyko! If it's back Vitalis, who am I to stay away! You should hear a cheering!"

"Everybody's happy!"

"For the first time down there they celebrating peace without a war.

"This is really good.

"And this is also you reporter, signing off and bidding you good night!"

And down below on the soap box was still screaming the orator:

"Beware from the Atomic bomb . . . . beware! I tell you! It now holds mankind in his hands the means from his destruction! !"

What came in this moment interruptions:

"Just a second, pal!"

Standing in front from the soap was Fenimore Figgits. Still draped by him around the neck was a busted microphone.

The left arm was hanging in a slink. A black eye he was featuring. And on the top from his head was reversely indented in print from a flying paper-weight the words:

COMMITTEE FROM PEACEFUL ARBITRATION

Up on the soap box gave a jump Mister Figgits. And to the orator he said:

"You got slightly cockeyed you facts my friend! Allow a man

from experience to put you hep to just what could destroy the world. Atomic bombs you need? Don't be a child! With a cream puff you could destroy the world. . . . With a chocolate eclair! With a bobby pin . . . . yi! When I stop to think what it could do a woman with a bobby pin . . . . I shudder. With a thought, a wrong one let loose, you could destroy the world. With a impulse a evil one . . . . with a desire a dumb one! Or with a thought a impulse, a desire which is right, but which the people fail to understand! On account they fearful to admit they understanding. Speeches I couldn't make fancy . . . . all I knowing is a little poem from my schoolhood days. It would behoof all statesmen kings with leaders they should study it. With you permission I'll reciting it:

> "*Kind hearts, they the gardens;*
> *Kind thoughts, they the roots.*
> *Kind words, they the flowers;*
> *Kind deeds, they the fruits!*"

What in this moment it accustard him a individual with a question, so:

"Pardon me, pal. But now that it's finished by you the spring planting, allow me I should asking you a question. Do you consist from Fenimore Figgits?"

"I do!"

"Can you indemnify yourself?"

"I can. You'll give a look here on top from my head so you'll see on the top is reversely stamped printing. Here is a hand mirror. Backwards you'll read it please . . . . What does it saying?"

"Committee from Peaceful Arbitration! This is for me enough proof, pal. You Figgits all right. So do you also know a dame a blonde one, entitled Sugar?"

"I do. We met during a obsequies. The guest from honor was a doctor."

"You went together with this Sugar to the doctor?"

"I did!"

"Why did you went!"

"On account from Sugar's brother!"

"Ha ha ha! You kill me pal. On account from Sugar's brother you went with her to a doctor. Better take it on the skip, sweetypie, or on account her brother, you'll go next time to a hospital!"

"I fail," responded Mister Figgits, "to attaching to you crack any meaning. Also do I fail to find in it a sauce from levity!"

"So allow me pal, in this case I should do the attaching. I'll just attach to you this paper . . . . which in turn will make attachments on your bank roll . . . . Papa. . . . . It consists the paper from a summons. On behalf from the little lady entitled

Sugar. . . . . Papa! A dollar apiece I garner for serving them
. . . . Pop!"

"Papa!" gave exclamations in dismay Mister Figgits.

"Hm you getting pale, ha? My my! And at your age too.
Altho in some ways is a compliment . . . . Is no, Pop? On the
other hand there was once a professor who had twins at the
age from a hundred and two . . . . So you not bagging a record
. . . . you just bagging a lawsuit . . . . ha ha ha. . . . ."

"Stop winking on me . . . . with nudging me by the ribs . . . .
with calling me Papa!"

"Take it easy, Pop . . . . ha ha . . . . Sugar Papa . . . . Sugar
Mamma . . . . Sugar baby! That's a joke, son . . . . I mean
Father . . . .! So what! What's to a guy like you a few hundred
grand to settling on the brat? A big operator like you . . . . with a
million bucks!"

"I . . . . got . . . . a . . . . million . . . . bucks?"

"Pretty sly, Pop. Under cover you played it smart all along
. . . . Living in a trap a cheap one . . . . Suits from one flight up
you wearing. Lunch by hot dog stands you grabbing. And all the
time is stashed away by you a cool million fish!"

"A . . . . cool . . . . million!"

"Cool is right. It ain't so hot no more. Not since it found out
Sugar's lawyer all about it. A sharp cookie that boy. Slickest
mouthpiece in the racket. Guy entitled Fergy. . . . . Help, quick!
. . . . It fainted Mister Figgits!"

7

$\mathcal{H}$OME IN THE little frame house, in the love seat, the deserted one, sat Phoebe Figgits. Present was her best girl friend, Ruthie, trying she should make for Phoebe consolations.

Pictures from Fenimore once again was hanging frontwards

Remorseful sat Phoebe.

"I could have sworn it followed me a jealous ape!"

on the wall. Wistfully gazed Phoebe at the pictures from the vanished Fenimore. A shrew she was, perhaps, but sad with poignant now she looked. And like a school child penitent she spoke:

"It's all my fault, Ruthie . . . . my fault only! . . . . Jealous, mean, vindictish, did I was . . . . And now I drove him off . . . . My Fenimore . . . . Suspicious did I was . . . . so now I lost him. My Fenimore! Me . . . . myself alone . . . . I . . . . I drove him off. How I miss him now!"

"Try," gave consolations Ruthie, "two snorts from vodka in a crock tomato juice. You'll feeling better, dear!"

"Oh, if I could only hear him snore once more! If only he had bottled up a couple snores before he left. So when nostalgic I would get, I could uncork them. How I picked on him . . . . hated him when it came out from the blonde flooze the law-suit . . . . With his million dollars secret ones . . . . Guilty I be-lieved him then . . . . Until that day. When I was reconnoitering underneath the Frigidaire . . . . And I found the secret paper . . . . My Fenimore! ! For them a dummy, with a stooge! . . . . the rats! All these years taking for them raps! Sticking out for them his neck! . . . . Fizwell the weasel! Now I know for what he came with all the build-ups! Making me with his fast pitches, crazy! Languages from flowers . . . . first pink flush from dawn . . . . The mealy mouthed, low-down trap handed fink! I tell you Ruthie darling . . . . it made me almost crazy, his romancings. Spinning was my head . . . . Till I began to think that I was see-ing things . . . . Hallucinations I was getting . . . . that it was following me nights a ape . . . . a jealous one! Thursday nights especial.

A wild ape—such nightmares! I could have sworn almost it was real . . . . A bread knife in its hand . . . . and in the eyes a gleam from jealous rage. So terrified I was, I slept for nights with both eyes open!"

"Try dearie, this one," gave further consolations, Ruthie, "a

"I slept with both eyes open."

tumbler bourbon in a seidel beer. It'll cheer you up!"

"I don't care what he did . . . . even though I knew he didn't do it . . . . I just want him back. So considerate he was. Calling always on the phone to ask if something he could bring me home. Of course he always got it cock-eyed. I would say, yes, bring me home some Bi-So-Dol . . . . and home he would come at night, all smiles, lugging on his back a bicycle, a new one! Bright with shiny . . . . Such a dope, but so good-hearted. Outside maybe careless, easy going, mild, insipid. . . . . But inside, a thinker, a philosopher, a man from iron will with courage!"

"Too bad," gave consolations Ruthie, "that he didn't turned himself inside out a little sooner. Here, try this one, dearie . . . . Six fingers rum mixed with a pitcher gin with onions."

"Personals I got now running in the paper for days. He should come home to me. Two weeks Ruthie . . . . sniff sniff. A total vanish! Not a sign from him . . . . hide nor toupee . . . .! Hiding in disgrace some place . . . . Little knowing he is now a famous man. A hero! Spirit from the people it calls him editorials . . . . The voice from the common man . . . . The words from a Prophet. 'With a cream puff you could wreck the world!' Look from his poem Kind Hearts a write up! Reporters they sent to his native town to interview by him the old school teacher, with the Fire Chief, with the village cobbler, who is also there the the oldest inhabitant. Read here, Ruthie in the magazine":

It greeted your reporter, in the native town from Fenimore Figgits, the oldest inhabitant, entitled Titus Moody. Said Mister Moody:

Howdy bub! Do I recall old Fogart Figgits, by Fenimore the great grandfather? I do. First Figgits what it settled here. Came in eighty-six. Started sitting on a flag pole. Whole town snickered. Said old Fogart sure was touched. Dam broke. Town flooded. Everybody drowned but Fogart. Too high up for the water to reach him . . . . So long, bub!

And from his old school teacher Effie Appletrap:

Fenimore I don't recalling, but his Uncle Feathergill . . . . Yi! Wotta man! Frustrated ball player, he was. All day long on Main and Market he stole bases. Hydrants he slid into, telegraph poles. Traffic lights with ash cans. Up he would get. Off he would dust himself. Bows he would take . . . . Wotta man! . . . . He also smelt so nice!

"Imagine Ruthie . . . . Always was us Figgits personalities. And now is gone my Fenimore . . . . The divorce with alimony? Just to keep that weasel Fizwell he should getting on the dough his hooks. That's the only reason I go through with it. Not that I would touch a penny from the filthy trash. Just that it should simper Fizwell a trifle in his own stew. Look here is for Fenimore more honors. It wants the Country Club we should be now there members!"

"Yi yi yi! The Country Club. Phoebe darling . . . . you don't mean it!"

"The Committee used to snooted me!"

"But now! Debs with bobby soxers!"

"This morning gives a ring the bell. Standing there is the committee what for years it snooted me!"

"That hoity-toity bunch from bags!"

"You should saw there·slick chicks too. With debs with bobby soxers yet with albums. Autograph albums, Ruthie, it should make in them inscriptures, Fenimore . . . . The dashing romantic swashbuckling Fenimore. The man from many loves with passions . . . . Papa Figgits. Would you believe it Ruthie?

"Barbecues! Credit cards from the biggest stores, hotels. Friends tell me it insists he should design for me a hat, Kenneth Popkins. Please Ruthie darling. You my best friend . . . . Not a word to a soul. Don't ever let it out that Fenimore is innocent from all the scandals . . . . or we dead socially!"

"Who me, dearie? Who do I ever see. I live up in the hills . . . . Hm, Barbecues . . . . Country Clubs! Does my dope from a husband ever get mixed up in a stink? Not him! Not Careful

Clarence! Oh no!"

What in this moment it gave on the doorbell a ring, and for Ruthie came calling Clarence to take her home. Greetings gave Ruthie to him:

"Oh, it's you, dope?"

Responses gave Clarence:

"Hello my love! From a Lodge Meeting I'm just coming. Here with me is witnesses to prove it. Pete with Mike. . . . ."

Over the head it gave him with a andiron a conk, Ruthie. Yells with proofs from innocence, gave Clarence. The more he gave proofs, the more he derived conks with the andiron. What impatiently gave exclamations Phoebe:

"Quiet please! Can't you see I'm busy compositing for the paper another personal. This time in poetry form. Maybe via poetry I'll getting back my Fenimore. Listen:

> *"Oh Fenimore, Oh Fenimore*
> *Come home to Phoebe, I implore!"*

8

IN A TERRIBLE state was now Mister Fizwell. From Fizwell, Wizwell, with Philpot, was Mister Fizwell the main ingredient. So now was by him the main headache.

In the study he sat. On the head was a ice-pack! On the chest

In a terrible state was Mister Fizwell.

a hot-water bag. In the hand a triple hooker straight rum. A relic from his youth in the Barbados. In front from him was itemizing a secretary a list from all the lawsuits against Mister Figgits. In which was implicated Mister Fizwell's million dollars. So it recited the secretary the list so:

From Sugar on behalf from a Bundle from Heaven, a coming one . . . . Two hundred with fifty thousand dollars.

For the Missus Figgits for divorce with alimony, with one half from the community property, which is assets from a million dollars . . . . Five hundred thousand dollars.

From the doctor's relatives with heirs. One hundred thousand dollars damages. Due to lousing up by him the funeral, · nd causing to the doctor humiliation with embarrassment.

For a cop, on behalf from a broken jaw, by Felix in the Cafe . . . . Twenty-five thousand dollars damages . . . . with sixty-five cents bus fare.

From Felix for a Cafe, a wrecked one . . . . Two hundred with six thousand dollars.

Nimbly however in the meantime was working by Mister Fizwell the fertile brain, what to himself he was figuring so:
"From the blonde is the whole thing obviously a frame. A couple house dicks I could put here on the job. In two days they'll rustling up enough on her, so she'll have to catch the first rocket to the Moon. This way is saved two hundred with fifty grand . . . . less expenses. With the cop, the doctor's family, and with Felix we could making out from Court a deal. Off I'll pay them with that satchel full from phoney dough. And then I'll notify the F.B.I. that it's operating here in town a ring

from counterfeiters. No cost . . . . and we doing a favor to J. Edgar.

"This is leaving the only stumbling block Missus Figgits. . . . . So for this is now presenting itself to my mind a solution, far from unpleasant. For the divorce let her sue him. Boy this is good. Five hundred grand she'll collecting . . . . Yi! Now you getting places Fizzy! Pitches I made her already romantic ones. Good! Sweet she is naturally on me by now! . . . . Boy, does this getting better! My own battle axe it's time I gave gradually already a kick out. Back from Reno will be coming by this time the EX-Missus Figgits. With a half a million fish yet! Neatly will it glove-tail with my plans. A swift pitch I'll slip the dame! Off the feet she'll be swept. Married we'll get in Mexico. Custardy from the dough I'll grab at once. Then the little Spaniorita in Tampico. I'll give a buzz . . . . Yi yi! Still a noodle Fizzy! . . . . But first I better scooting over to the Missus Figgits with a line, a fast one, it shouldn't cool the pitch! A bottle Pernod with a copy Indian Love Lyrics, I better take along. . . . . Oh . . . . boy do I got a hangover. Better with a cup from coffee I should fortify myself before I go."

What it gave a roar Mister Fizwell:

"Ingrid! Ingrid! . . . . Where could it was that fool ape from a maid. Oh. there you are. Quick! A cup coffee! Well, don't stand there mooning on me like a baboon! Coffee! Quick!"

Tremblingly it made Ingrid a cup coffee. Into the coffee she dropped with a populating heart, two from Pasha's Potent Love Pills.

Upon a tray to Mister Fizwell she brought the cup coffee.

"Good grief!" he gave a roar. "Must you spill all over me the coffee. You shaking like a aspirin leaf, girl. Take better tomorrow off!"

What to herself kept tremulously repeating Ingrid.

"Captivate, charm, allure. He's yours girls . . . . Yours!"

Out from the house gave strides Mister Fizwell. Inside was

Tremblingly she gave a drop in the coffee the pills.

firmamenting in him the coffee with the Love Pills. Next door in front from the porch was sweeping the sidewalk Begonia, the maid. A bend she gave over to gather in the dust pan, the dust. To a sizzle came in Mister Fizwell at this moment the Love Pills. Passing also, was a bus load from Policemen, to the Policemen's Annual Picnic en route. . . . . So dun't esk!

Resignations Mister Fizwell had to make from all the corporations from which he consisted from Chairman from the Board. Out it carried him on a desk-chair four soldiers. And so soon what he resigned was promptly settled fourteen strikes. In all the factories was started up at once production. Stabilized became economy. Up overnight went all over the country housing projects. Released was controls. Inflation gave a cease. Broken hearted was Ingrid. And home in her love seat was Phoebe finishing to Fenimore the poem so:

A bend over gave Begonia.

Come back to me my darling, to the love seat which
we sat in.
Nibbling on Sundays anchovies, on cinnamon buns
au gratin.
Come back to you sorrowing Phoebe. Come back once
more to my arms.
And the rest from my days in the love seat, I'll eating
you up with my charms. . . . .

Phoebe. . . . .

What in this moment gave a yell on the streets the newsboys all over town:

EXTRA! EXTRA! BOTTLE FOUND FLOATING
IN RIVER . . . . MESSAGE INSIDE . . . . I SHOULDA
ATE THE ECLAIR. . . . . F.F.

A swoon gave Missus Figgits.

9

BY A DOCK in front from the water, from which is derived the expression waterfront, stood a low dive. This dive consisted from a saloon. And the saloon was now inhabited by the Press, it should be by them set up inside, temporary headquarters. Adjacent to the Press Headquarters was located, in the river, the spot where it was found floating, from Mister Figgits in the bottle, the message:

I shoulda ate the eclair!

All along the front from the river, on top from the piers, was ensembled Fire Trucks, with Police first-aid rusticators, with squad cops, with grappling hooks.

Present was from the Police the Commissioner. Also from the City, His Honor, alias the Mayor. Reverently stood by respectful crowds, waiting they should exonerate Mister Figgits from the river. Old with young they came. One man with a bulldog still embedded in the leg. "Just say a friend" he told reporters. "I was on my way to the doctor to have this dog extracted . . . . but my respects I had to pay to the poor erstwhile Mister Figgits."

Twenty troops from Boy Scouts gave in chorus recitations Kind Hearts. It should be for Fenimore a tribute. From his trial it

169

sat the Jury Potpecker with Snackery, Hodge with Boggleweiss with Gazzwatts. Tranifatts with Ishkadoo with Keewis. Even Missus Rasselass! In a Jury box a draped one. Draped with black the box they sat in. Wearing dunce caps all the Jury. It should be for Mister Figgits tributes. Overhead flew a plane, making in the sky with sky writing the immortal words from Mister Figgits:

"With a cream puff you could wreck the world!"

On the outsquirts from the crowd was from the Night Court present the Judge who owned the fat wife. Incockatoo he stood, wearing on the eyes dark glasses. What to himself he gave a mutter:

"If for my wife they were fishing, they would need gradually a derrick!"

In the middle from two nurses, with a attendant on each side yet, holding a bottle smelling salts, sat poor Phoebe Figgits. Sadly it gave in her direction a shake with his head the Mayor. To the Police Commissioner he spoke, without moving the lips, a trick which he learned from a friend, a resident from Folsom:

"Two weeks down there. Hopeless. A fish couldn't live in that water. Poor Missus Figgits! Night with day. Don't eat . . . . Don't sleep. Hardly powders her nose. Sad boys! Ask her with my compliments if she would like maybe a Good Humor?"

Down it sank again the grappling hooks. Up it gave a yank the cops.

Nothing!

Nothing! All the way down through the waiting crowd echoed the word. Nothing! Into the Press headquarters in the saloon. Nothing! Till it reached the bar. At which spot it ceased everybody to say, Nothing! Cynically gave suggestions a gentleman from the press:

"If those cops would try with a worm on the hooks instead from the fancy fly-casting, they might get better results."

"Grapple away men!" gave orders the Mayor. Grim with

170

stern was knit by him the brow. "Grapple away! We must re-
covering him!"

"Boo hoo hoo!" gave broken heartedly sobs Phoebe, "They talking about him like he was an old parlor sofa! Two weeks down
there . . . . without rubbers yet . . . . Boo hoo hoo!"

"Grapple again, boys!" rang out from the Mayor orders. In
the river it gave a sink again the grappling hooks.

So while was sinking in the river the hooks, and while was
waiting with baited breath, on top from the docks, the ensemblage, underneath from the dock, in a old abandoned wharf-
rat shack, was going on a strange senance.

Secretly hidden was the shack, a old river pirate's hide-out.
By the bottom from a flight from rotting steps, across from two
water-soaked planks, full from seaweed with barnacles.

And inside the shack, instead from lying on the bottom from
the river, so was tied up with ropes with wires in a chair, for
two weeks Fenimore Figgits.

Snarling in front from him loitered his captor. Dimly it flick-
ered in a empty whisky bottle, a candle. In the glare from the
candle it gave omnibusly with his beetle brows a glower, the
captor.

"Yi!" thought Mister Figgits. "If it would only blow out again
for a minute the candle! . . . . Then I could scribble another
note with a pencil in my teeth, and in a bottle I could sneak it
again out from the window, it should float in the river, it should
be from me a clue to the Police, my whereabouts!"

What in this moment gave a snarl again the captor.

"Well, jerk, will you or will you not gonna do the right thing
by my little sister, Sugar? Or do I dump you into the drink?"

Replied Mister Figgits:

"I must repeating, you are all wrong, sir, in you diagnosis
from this matter!"

Up in a rage it gave a jump the brother.

"Look, muzzler! I try with you I should be eminently fair.

171

"Grapple away men!" gave orders the Mayor!

With a strong sense from justice, aided only by this rubber hose, and this pair pliers, I try to prying out from you the truth. In a nice way I'm trying. So confess . . . . I beg from you . . . . confess . . . . and with my blessing do by Sugar the right thing."

"Look, pal," gave responses Mister Figgits, "once before a certain party tried to get me to confessing to a deed which I didn't did! Fortunately for humanity, in this moment, Vitalis came back. Do I make myself a little not transparent? So better take a tip and chop away from my dogs the cement."

"Please, Mister Figgits," protested the brother. "Before it really hardens the cement, come clean. I appealing to you sense from honor . . . . as a family man. I too am also a family man. Ah yes . . . . self-made yet . . . . from a poorish boy up! By us on the family mc cutcheon was never before such a blot! Always I worked hard. Easy it didn't was!"

"Nothing worth while in this world," made philosophies Mister Figgits, "is easy!"

"You said it pal! Struggles, early ones, I had. I could remember now . . . . if you'll wouldn't mind my boring you . . . . my early days. Me with Marm . . . . with Sugar just a little tot in the crib. Wotta word, crib! What memories! Cold. Hungry. Oftentimes without a reefer in the joint. Couldn't paying on the Sweet Marie, the rent . . . . Sweet Marie is to you Figgy, a Tommy-gun, alias a Riveter . . . . a Chopper. Yep, times there was we couldn't pay the rent on Sweet Marie. But Marmaduke was patient . . . . he had in me great faith . . . . Just the same was pretty tough the going. Had to even borrow from my brother-in-law his brass knuckles. Boy, was they a lousy fit! Ha ha! Had once a snapshot taken in them for a gag . . . . Right after a little mugging job. Boy did I have years later compulsions from laughing at that snap. Yep, oftentimes I laughing now. But then! . . . . Did I was oftentimes discouraged! Ready I was to chuck it all and get by a milk route a job. Then it would say to me Marm . . . . Hmmm, you should have known Marm, Figgy! She would love

Tied up was Mister Figgits in the shack.

"In a nice way, I try to prying out from you the truth."

you too. I could see her now . . . . this very minute . . . . sitting
in the rocker, making brooms. Boy could Marm make a broom!
With a set license plates . . . . with burlap sacks yet! So it would
say to me Marm:

'Don't give up, Frog-eye. Keep trying boy. For me!'

"Hungry. Cold. I could remember once, I held open for Yippy
the Mope a taxicab door. Me, a ragged punk. Snowing bitter
cold it was, and out was coming Yippy, gaily from the Opera,
with a crowd Society folk. 'Here, kid! . . . . ' he tosses me a dime!
. . . . 'Go get youself a shave!' Mania from Heaven it was! But
Marm said:

'Don't spend this dime Frog-eye! Not *this* one!'

"Till this day I got it. Thin it's worn till it could read through
it a palm, a Gypsy. Oftentimes I was tempted to spend it for a
slug . . . . but Marm's words would came back to me . . . . Heh.
Today I could have three times a day with each meal a magnus

from champagne . . . . although I still preferring a bathtub from gin . . . . But then . . . . in them days! Hungry! Cold! Ready to give up . . . . Then it would say to me Marm:

'Don't give up Frog-eye. Try once more. For me! If you take now that job by the milk route . . . . Curtains! Smile boy! Imagine that you sticking up the Mint . . . . and that all these Tommy-gun slugs is golden ignatzes! Try once more, boy!'

"So once more I gave a try. A little job I landed . . . . a tiny one. Just to mixing in a barrel the cement bath for a snatched banker what refused to pony up the ransom. Just like I mixed here now for you. Nothing much! But you should saw the look in Marm's eyes! Just mixing with a broom handle cement. But it caught from the big boy the eye. Something in the way I handled it. Soon came bigger jobs. A few dry cleaning joints to squirt some acid on! A bakery to knock over. Then from a lumber yard a payroll. Then a bank . . . . with a postoffice. Then . . . . Success! And now in my reclining days . . . . this disgrace . . . . So, why you don't please do by Sugar the right thing!"

"I thinking it over," gave replies Mister Figgits. But he was only acting a part. In reality this remark consisted from a stall. On account while Frog-eye was making his autobiography, Mister Figgits was throwing secretly out from the window, first his wallet, then his hat, then his coat with pants, then gradually his only pair from shorts. So each time on the docks when it gave the Police a yank up the hooks with all the personal momentums, it would burst out Phoebe with sobs, racking ones.

"His wallet . . . . his coat . . . . his hat . . . . his pants . . . . his shorts . . . . Boohoo-hoo!"

Down in the shack Frog-eye gave on his wrist-watch synchronization. With snarls he turned to Mister Figgits:

"Okay, sneezer! You asked for it. You now on you way to the Happy Dumping Grounds!"

Desperately gave Mister Figgits a wiggle with a squirm with a leap out from the window. Flying tackles made Frog-eye, after

Secretly threw Mister Figgits out his shorts.

"His shorts!" gave sobs heart-broken Phoebe.

him. Into the ropes with wires with the barrel cement they both became fascinated, and to the bottom from the river with a splash sank the whole business.

"Hold it boys!" gave a yell a cop with a grappling hook. "I think we got something!"

On top from the crowd fell a hush.

"They got him," came in whispers awed ones.

"Hoist away men!" gave a bark the Mayor. While with respect, his hat he doffed. Followed suit the crowd, with a silence a tremulous one.

Up from the river gave a hoist the cops the hooks.

Hushed with silent stood the crowd. From the Boy Scouts with the Girl Scouts Glee Club softly came a chanting

Up came Fenimore with Frog-eye fighting.

Kind hearts are the gardens;
Kind thoughts are the roots;
Kind words are the flowers;
Kind deeds are the fruits.

Out from the river rose the grappling hooks. Up came murkily from the water objects bulky ones. Wiggling, dripping, squirming. Entangled both with ropes with wires . . . . trying both to kill each other. . . . . Fenimore with Frog-eye, fighting!

A swoon gave Phoebe on the dock.

At the same moment, it appeared on the outsquirts from the crowd, Fergy with Sugar.

"Grab him!" gave yells Mister Figgits from the hook. Surmounted in a moment was Fergy with cops. While accusingly it pointed a finger on him Fenimore.

"Out with the truth!"

180

"Slap him on a lie detector," gave a bark the Mayor. While to Fergy the Police Commissioner gave such a kick in the ankle, what it broke him in a half almost the leg.

"Talk, rat!" he ordered.

Talking started Fergy. Completely he dissolved from guilt Fenimore. What Phoebe was revived in time that she should hear it all.

"I knew it," smiled she bravely through the tears!

On kept spouting Fergy. Till came exclamations from the Mayor.

"For the love from Pete, boys! Rip him off that lie detector! If he keeps on singing it will have to leave town gradually the whole *Who's Who!* Mayor, I'll then remain of myself."

From Philpot was the ending sad. From the metal from the dishpan it turned gradually his face blue. So, in a Circus he became a Blue Man. Wizwell fell in the excitement in a man-hole. What till this day, they probing for him. And Fizwell was grabbed desperately by the lovelorn Ingrid in her arms, and away she ran with him to Borneo.

And away she ran with him to Borneo.

But nothing of all this, heard Fenimore with Phoebe, who lovingly enwraptured stood entangled in each others arms. Then it shook hands sportingly Fenimore with Frog-eye, with promises to look each other up yet! And home it started Fenimore with Phoebe.

The million dollars was donated by Fenimore, to build for families with children Housing Projects.

And home he walked with Phoebe arm in arm. No longer in the front walked Mister Figgits. No longer in the back trailed Phoebe. But, side by side with arms entwined, they gave into the house a vanish. Making future plans to open up a roadside Tavern! What should be Felix by them Maitre-Domo!

And together in the love seat they lived happily ever after. . . . .

And in the love seat they lived happily ever after.